Geometric Terminology

Across

3. An angle measuring 180°.
5. Non–coplanar, non–intersecting lines.
6. Two angles that add to 90°.
8. In a right triangle, one of the shorter sides.
9. Lines that form right angles.
10. An angle measuring less than 90°.
11. Congruent angles formed by intersecting lines.
12. A polygon with all sides equal.
15. Longest side of a right triangle.

Down

1. Triangle with at least two congruent sides.
2. An angle measuring 90°.
4. Coplanar lines that never intersect.
5. Two angles that add to 180°.
6. Equal.
7. Triangle with no equal sides.
13. An angle measuring more than 90°.
14. Number of sides in a quadrilateral.

Word List

leg
skew
acute
obtuse
scalene
isosceles
equilateral
hypotenuse
perpendicular
complementary
supplementary
congruent
parallel
straight
vertical
right
four

MP4057

Angles Formed by Parallel Lines

If two parallel lines are cut by a transversal, the resulting angles are either congruent or supplementary.

<u>congruent angles</u>
vertical angles
corresponding angles
alternate interior angles
alternate exterior angles

<u>supplementary angles</u>
adjacent angles
same–side interior angles
same–side exterior angles

Find the measure of the angles using the given information. Match the measure with its corresponding letter and fill in the blanks to reveal the only non–presidents to appear on U.S. currency.

1. **If** $\angle 1 = 135°$, $\angle 2 =$ _____ .

2. **If** $\angle 3 = 62°$, $\angle 6 =$ _____ .

3. **If** $\angle 13 = 130°$, $\angle 16 =$ _____ .

4. **If** $\angle 9 = 110°$, $\angle 13 =$ _____ .

5. **If** $\angle 9 = 110°$, $\angle 14 =$ _____ .

6. **If** $\angle 10 = 60°$, $\angle 15 =$ _____ .

7. **If** $\angle 4 = 105°$, $\angle 5 =$ _____ .

8. **If** $\angle 4 = 105°$, $\angle 6 =$ _____ .

9. **If** $\angle 11 = 65°$, $\angle 14 =$ _____ .

10. **If** $\angle 9 = 125°$, $\angle 15 =$ _____ .

11. **If** $\angle 10 = 52°$, $\angle 3 =$ _____ .

12. **If** $\angle 7 = 83°$, $\angle 14 =$ _____ .

13. **If** $\angle 8 = 113°$, $\angle 13 =$ _____ .

14. **If** $\angle 12 = 140°$, $\angle 4 =$ _____ .

15. **If** $\angle 16 = 100°$, $\angle 3 =$ _____ .

16. **If** $\angle 9 = 100°$, $\angle 1 =$ _____ .

17. **If** $\angle 6 = 68°$, $\angle 11 =$ _____ .

Angles in diagram are for reference purposes only. Angles are not precise.

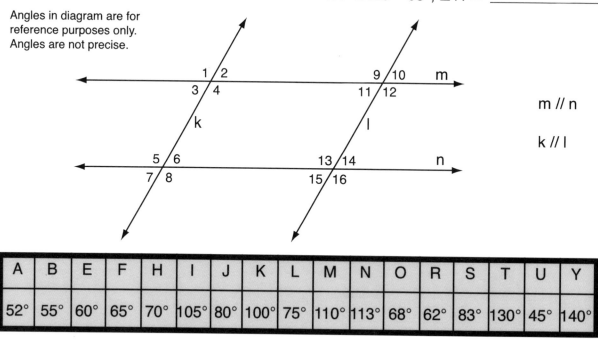

m // n

k // l

A	B	E	F	H	I	J	K	L	M	N	O	R	S	T	U	Y
52°	55°	60°	65°	70°	105°	80°	100°	75°	110°	113°	68°	62°	83°	130°	45°	140°

___ ___ ___ ___ ___ ___ ___ ___ ___ ___ ___ ___ ___ .
12 1 12 11 13   10   11 13 3 5 17 13 14

AND

___ ___ ___ ___ ___ ___ ___ ___ ___ ___ ___ ___ ___ ___ ___ ___
10 6 13 15 11 4 7 13   9 2 11 13 16 8 7 13

Triangle Side Theorem

The sum of the lengths of any two sides of a triangle is greater than the length of the third side.

Determine if segments of the given lengths can make a triangle. If they can, write the corresponding letter in the blanks below.

1, 2, 3 A	3, 4, 5 J	3, 9, 11 U	11, 12, 25 N	2, 2, 3 L
7, 9, 12 I	7, 7, 14 N	3, 7, 9 A	4, 10, 12 M	6, 7, 15 E
3, 3, 8 B	8, 8, 15 O	7, 11, 16 R	1, 18, 24 O	11, 22, 30 G
6, 12, 20 L	6, 8, 12 A	14, 16, 35 I	9, 13, 22 K	13, 15, 25 N

Who was the first successful woman architect?

___ ___ ___ ___ ___ ___ ___ ___ ___ ___ ___

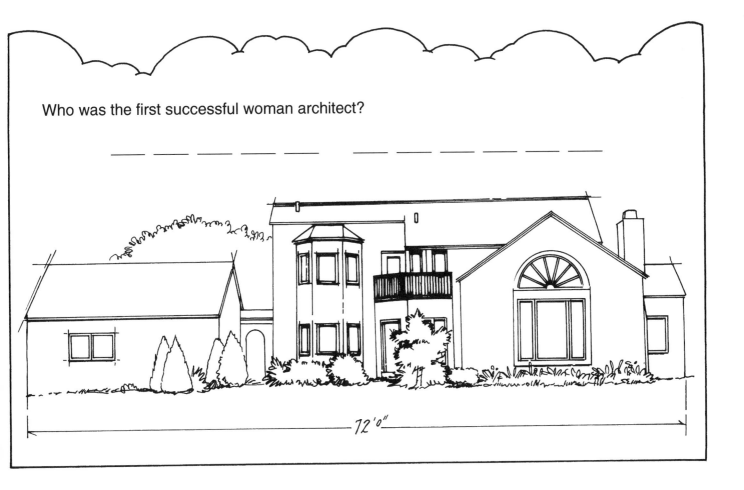

72'0"

MP4057

Angles of a Triangle

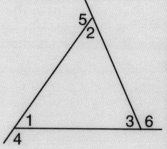

→The three angles in a triangle add to 180°: (∠1 + ∠2 + ∠3 = 180°).

   If each side is extended in one direction, exterior angles are formed: (∠4, ∠5, and ∠6).

→An interior angle and its adjacent exterior angle are supplements: (∠1 + ∠4 = 180°).

→The measure of an exterior angle is equal to the sum of its remote interior angles: (∠2 + ∠3 = ∠4).

→All three exterior angles add to 360°: (∠4 + ∠5 + ∠6 = 360°).

Place the letter in the blank above its measure to reveal an interesting fact about our 49th state.

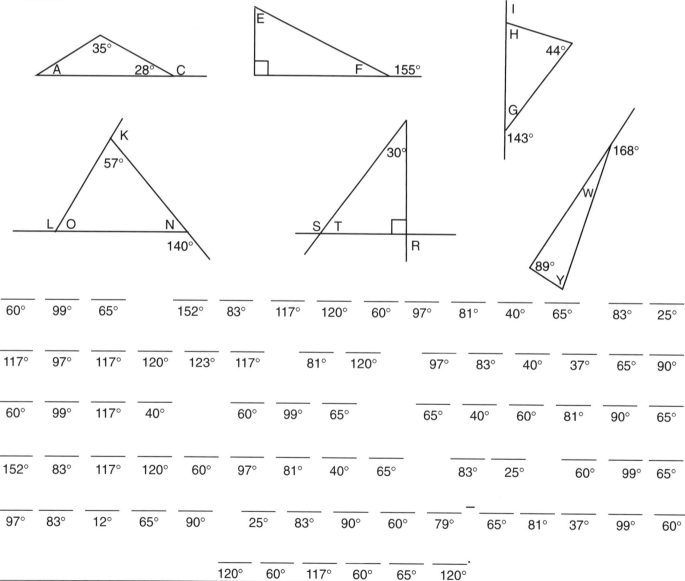

___ ___ ___   ___ ___ ___ ___ ___ ___ ___ ___ ___   ___ ___
60° 99° 65°   152° 83° 117° 120° 60° 97° 81° 40° 65°   83° 25°

___ ___ ___ ___ ___ ___   ___ ___   ___ ___ ___ ___ ___ ___
117° 97° 117° 120° 123° 117° 81° 120°   97° 83° 40° 37° 65° 90°

___ ___ ___ ___   ___ ___ ___   ___ ___ ___ ___ ___ ___
60° 99° 117° 40°   60° 99° 65°   65° 40° 60° 81° 90° 65°

___ ___ ___ ___ ___ ___ ___ ___ ___   ___ ___   ___ ___ ___
152° 83° 117° 120° 60° 97° 81° 40° 65°   83° 25°   60° 99° 65°

___ ___ ___ ___ ___   ___ ___ ___ ___ ___   ___ ___ ___ ___ ___
97° 83° 12° 65° 90°   25° 83° 90° 60° 79°   65° 81° 37° 99° 60°

                    ___ ___ ___ ___ ___ ___.
                    120° 60° 117° 60° 65° 120°

Triangle Inequalities

In one triangle, the longest side is opposite the largest angle and the shortest side is opposite the smallest angle.

When given the lengths of two sides of a triangle, the length of the third side must be greater than their difference, but less than their sum.

Fill in the chart.

	lengths of two sides of a triangle	third side must be greater than	less than
1.	7 and 12		
2.	15 and 17		
3.	20 and 25		
4.	3 and 4		
5.	9 and 15		
6.	10 and 10		

Place the letter of the largest angle or longest side in the blanks below. Diagrams are not drawn to scale; base your answer on measurements given.

7.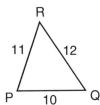

8.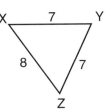

9.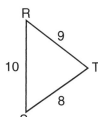

10.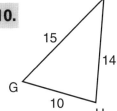

11.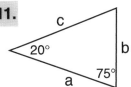

12.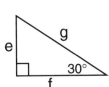

13.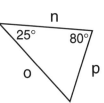

14.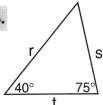

15.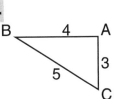

16.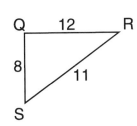

Name a Greek mathematician who is most famous for his theorem about right triangles.

___ ___ ___ ___ ___ ___ ___ ___ ___

Special Properties of Equilateral and Isosceles Triangles

A bisector divides something into two equal parts.

In an equilateral triangle, all sides are equal, which makes all three angles equal.

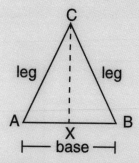

In an isosceles triangle, the bisector of the vertex angle is perpendicular to the base at its midpoint.

∠A and ∠B are <u>base angles</u> and are equal.
∠ACB is the <u>vertex angle</u>.

If $\overline{CX}$ bisects ∠ACB, then $\overline{CX} \perp \overline{AB}$ and X is the midpoint of $\overline{AB}$ (AX = XB).

Solve for the variables below. Shade the answer below to uncover the name of the first electronic digital computer produced in the United States.

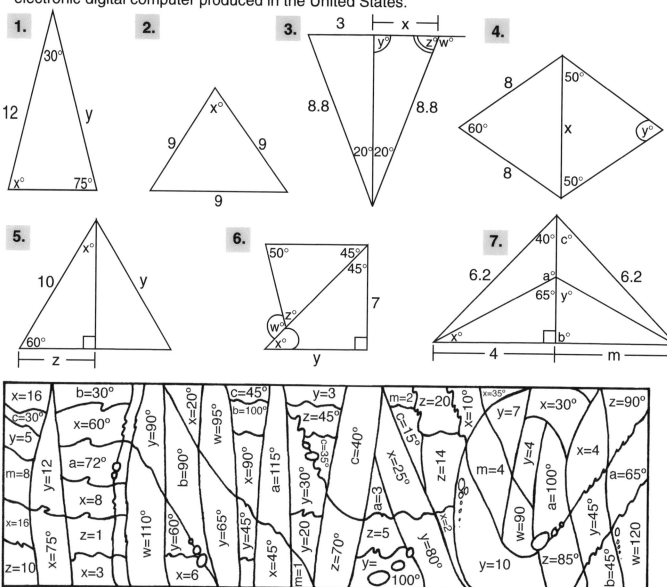

Algebra Review: Solving Equations

Steps for Solving Algebraic Equations

1. Simplify each side by
   —distributing
   —combining like terms
2. Move all variables to one side
3. Eliminate the constant using +/–
4. Eliminate the coefficient using x/÷

$$9(x+1)+2 = 4(x+8)-2x$$
$$9x+9+2 = 4x+32-2x$$
$$9x+11 = 2x+32$$
$$7x+11 = 32$$
$$7x = 21$$
$$x = 3$$

Solve the following algebraic equations. Follow the answers through the maze.

1. $3(x+5) = 2x+20$

2. $4(y-2) = 3(y+5)$

3. $9w+5 = 4(3w-1)$

4. $3g-5+9g = 4+15g+3$

5. $4(p-5) = 5(p-7)$

6. $3x+5 = 4-2x+6$

7. $4(m-3) = 6(m+1)$

8. $4(n+8)-3n = 42$

9. $2(t-7)-1 = -5(6-t)$

10. $7(2y-1)+3y = -3(y+2)+9$

11. $x = 2(10-x)+1$

12. $2(m+3)+2m = 5m$

13. $4c-3(c-8) = 47$

14. $3(x-5)-4(2x-4) = -2(x-11)$

START:

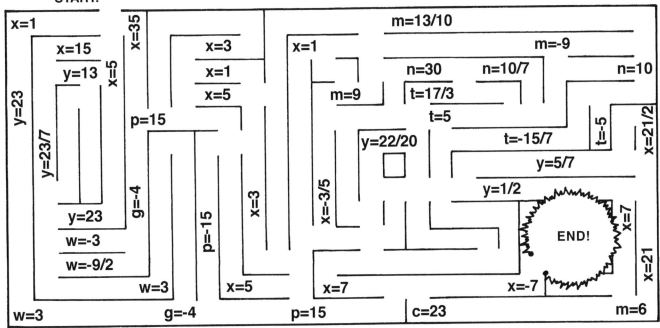

©Milliken Publishing Company

7

MP4057

Using Algebra to Solve for Angle Measures

Determine an algebraic equation for the given diagram. Solve for x. Locate and shade your answer in the puzzle to find the number of sides on a snowflake.

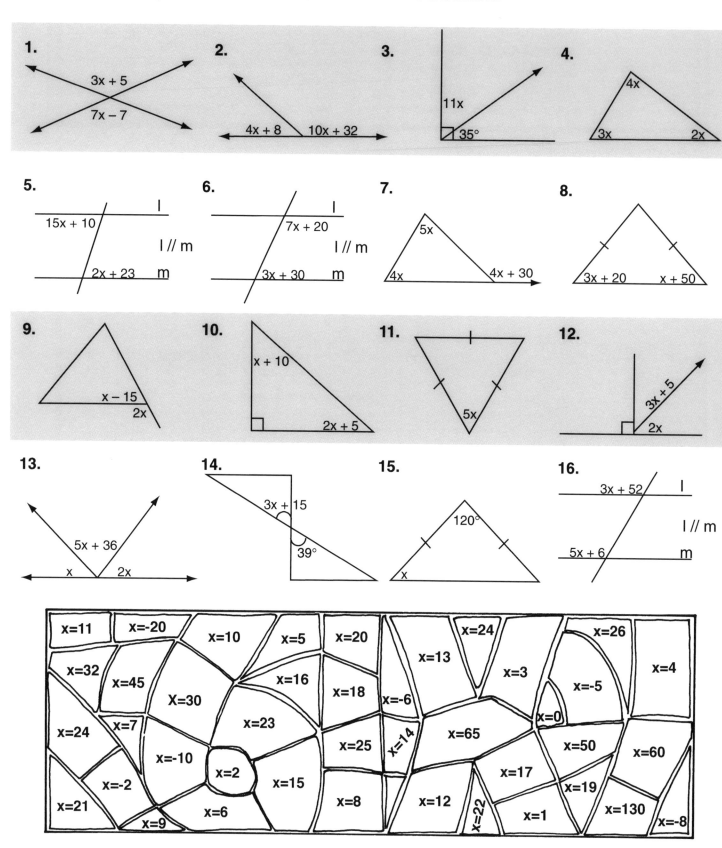

1.

$3x + 5$

$7x - 7$

2.

$4x + 8$ $10x + 32$

3.

$11x$

$35°$

4.

$4x$

$3x$ $2x$

5.

$15x + 10$ l

$l // m$

$2x + 23$ m

6.

$7x + 20$ l

$l // m$

$3x + 30$ m

7.

$5x$

$4x$ $4x + 30$

8.

$3x + 20$ $x + 50$

9.

$x - 15$

$2x$

10.

$x + 10$

$2x + 5$

11.

$5x$

12.

$3x + 5$

$2x$

13.

$5x + 36$

x $2x$

14.

$3x + 15$

$39°$

15.

$120°$

x

16.

$3x + 52$ l

$l // m$

$5x + 6$ m

x=11	x=-20	x=10	x=5	x=20	x=24	x=26
x=32	x=45		x=16	x=13	x=3	x=4
	X=30		x=18	x=-6	x=-5	
x=24	x=7	x=23		x=14	x=65	x=0	x=50	x=60
	x=-10	x=2	x=25		x=17	x=19	
x=-2		x=15	x=8	x=12	x=22	x=1	x=130
x=21	x=9	x=6				x=-8

©Milliken Publishing Company

8

MP4057

Using Algebra with Complements and Supplements

Remember:

$x =$ the angle

$90° - x =$ its complement

$180° - x =$ its supplement

Set up an equation for each problem, then solve for x. Use your answer for x to find the angle measures for the problem.

1. The complement of an angle is five times the measure of the angle itself. Find the angle and its complement.

2. The supplement of an angle is 30° less than twice the measure of the angle itself. Find the angle and its supplement.

3. The supplement of an angle is twice as large as the angle itself. Find the angle and its supplement.

4. The complement of an angle is 6° less than twice the measure of the angle itself. Find the angle and its complement.

5. Three times the measure of the supplement of an angle is equal to eight times the measure of its complement. Find the angle, its complement, and its supplement.

6. Two angles are congruent and complementary. Find their measures.

7. Two angles are congruent and supplementary. Find their measures.

8. The complement of an angle is twice as large as the angle itself. Find the angle and its complement.

9. The complement of an angle is 10° less than the angle itself. Find the angle and its complement.

10. The supplement of an angle is 20° more than three times the angle itself. Find the angle and its supplement.

Bisectors and Midpoints

An angle bisector	is a ray which divides an angle into two congruent angles.
A midpoint	is the point that divides a segment into two congruent segments.
A segment bisector	is a segment, ray, line, or plane that passes through the midpoint of a segment.

Refer to the diagrams. Solve for the variable. Find your answer in the decoder and fill in the letters to find what the c represents in the equation $E = mc^2$.

1. $\overrightarrow{OB}$ bisects $\angle AOC$.
   $m\angle 1 = 2x + 20$; $m\angle 2 = 5x + 5$.

2. $\overrightarrow{OC}$ bisects $\angle BOD$.
   $m\angle 2 = 3x - 7$; $m\angle 3 = 2x + 5$.

3. $\overrightarrow{OD}$ bisects $\angle COE$.
   $m\angle 3 = 8 - 5x$; $m\angle 4 = 2 - 6x$.

4. $\overrightarrow{OC}$ bisects $\angle AOE$.
   $m\angle 1 = 5a + 2$; $m\angle 2 = 2a - 7$; $m\angle 3 = 4a$; $m\angle 4 = 7$

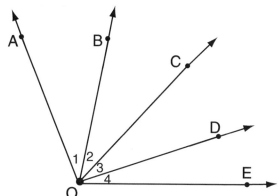

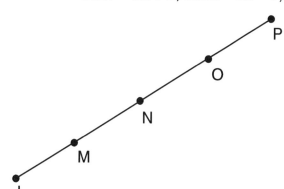

5. M is the midpoint of $\overline{LN}$. LM = 4 − 3x; MN = 7
6. N is the midpoint of $\overline{MO}$. MN = 3x − 4; NO = 17
7. O is the midpoint of $\overline{NP}$. NP = 40; OP = 2x + 8
8. N is the midpoint of $\overline{LP}$. LN = 30; NO = 3d
   OP = 6d + 12

9. EG = 6k + 8; GH = 4k + 28
10. $\angle FGD = 18x + 6$; $\angle DGH = 10x$
11. EG = 3p + 8; EH = 100

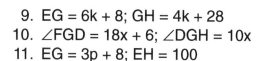

7	12	4	6	5	3	−1	14	10	−6	2
D	E	F	G	H	I	L	O	P	S	T

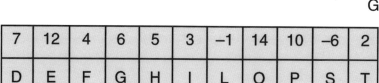

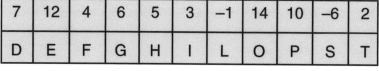

$\underline{}_{8} \ \underline{}_{1} \ \underline{}_{2} \ \underline{}_{3} \ \underline{}_{9} \ \underline{}_{2} \ \underline{}_{2} \ \underline{}_{6} \quad \underline{}_{11} \ \underline{}_{4}$

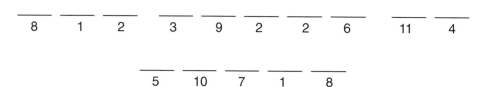

$\underline{}_{5} \ \underline{}_{10} \ \underline{}_{7} \ \underline{}_{1} \ \underline{}_{8}$

The Midpoint Formula

To find the midpoint between two ordered pairs, add the x–coordinates and divide by two; then do the same with the y–coordinates.

Example: Find the midpoint between (3, –6) and (7, –2).

$$\frac{3+7}{2} = \frac{10}{2} = 5 \quad \text{and} \quad \frac{-6+-2}{2} = \frac{-8}{2} = -4$$

The midpoint is (5, –4).

Find the midpoints for the following sets of ordered pairs. Then plot the midpoints on the graph below and connect them in the order of the problem numbers. You will reveal a mathematical symbol that was introduced in 1525 in a book about algebra titled *Die Coss*.

1. (–8, 3) and (–2, –5)

2. (–5, 3) and (–3, –3)

3. (–10, –6) and (2, 2)

4. (–2, 5) and (–4, –5)

5. (8, 1) and (–12, 3)

6. (7, –3) and (–7, 7)

7. (1, –8) and (3, 12)

8. (6, –4) and (2, 8)

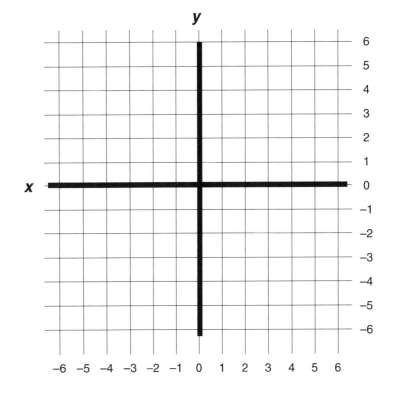

Special Segments in Triangles

A median of a triangle connects a vertex to the midpoint of the opposite side.

An altitude of a triangle is a segment drawn from a vertex perpendicular to the opposite side (or an extension of it).

or

A midline of a triangle connects two midpoints of two sides and is parallel to the third side. Its length is also half the length of the third side.

$$\overline{MN} \parallel \overline{PQ}$$
$$MN = \tfrac{1}{2} PQ$$

Refer to the diagrams. Find the answers in the decoder to reveal the name of the last major league baseball field to install lights for night games.

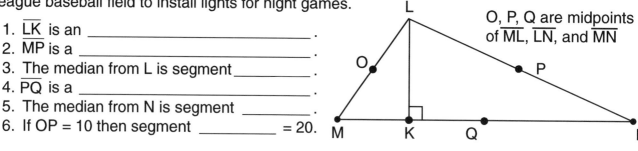

O, P, Q are midpoints of $\overline{ML}$, $\overline{LN}$, and $\overline{MN}$

1. $\overline{LK}$ is an _____ .
2. $\overline{MP}$ is a _____ .
3. The median from L is segment _____ .
4. $\overline{PQ}$ is a _____ .
5. The median from N is segment _____ .
6. If OP = 10 then segment _____ = 20.

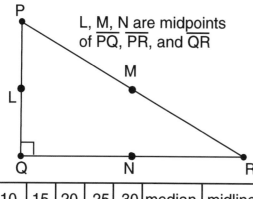

L, M, N are midpoints of $\overline{PQ}$, $\overline{PR}$, and $\overline{QR}$

7. The altitude from P is segment_____ .
8. If PL = 10, then the length of LQ is _____ .
9. If PQ = 30, then the length of MN is _____ .
10. If PM = 20, then the length of LN is _____ .
11. Segment LN is half the length of segment _____ .
12. ΔPQR is a _____ triangle.
13. If LM = 15, then the length of QR is _____ .
14. If the perimeter of ΔPQR = 50 units, the perimeter of ΔLMN would be _____ units.

10	15	20	25	30	median	midline	altitude	PQ	PR	MN	LQ	ON	right	isosceles
A	C	D	E	F	G	H	I	L	N	O	R	W	Y	Z

   5   3   1   2   7   14   12   13   1   14   7   10

   1   11   9   4   1   9   8   2   6

Multiplying and Simplifying Radical Expressions

Many radical expressions contain perfect squares which become whole numbers. To simplify a radical expression, factor the radical into the largest perfect square and another factor. Then simplify.

Example: $\sqrt{48} = \sqrt{16} \cdot \sqrt{3} = 4\sqrt{3}$

perfect square — other factor

To multiply radical expressions, follow these three steps:
I. Multiply whole numbers (if any)
II. Multiply radicals
III. Simplify the results

Example: $\left(4\sqrt{2}\right)\left(6\sqrt{2}\right) = 24\sqrt{4}$
$$= 24(2)$$
$$= 48$$

Simplify the following radical expressions and use the decoder to reveal the mathematician who introduced the radical sign.

1. $\left(3\sqrt{3}\right)\left(4\sqrt{2}\right)$

2. $\left(5\sqrt{2}\right)\left(6\sqrt{2}\right)$

3. $\left(4\sqrt{3}\right)\left(4\sqrt{3}\right)$

4. $\left(9\sqrt{2}\right)^2$

5. $\left(3\sqrt{3}\right)^2$

6. $\left(3\sqrt{5}\right)\left(\sqrt{10}\right)$

7. $\sqrt{90}$

8. $\sqrt{128}$

9. $\sqrt{63}$

10. $\left(\sqrt{45}\right)\left(\sqrt{20}\right)$

11. $\left(\sqrt{200}\right)^2$

48	200	162	$12\sqrt{6}$	$15\sqrt{2}$	$8\sqrt{2}$	60	27	30	$3\sqrt{10}$	$3\sqrt{7}$
C	D	F	H	I	L	O	R	S	T	U

___ ___ ___ ___ ___ ___ ___ ___ ___
3   1   5   6   10   7   2   4   4

___ ___ ___ ___ ___ ___ ___
5   9   11   2   8   4   4

The Pythagorean Theorem

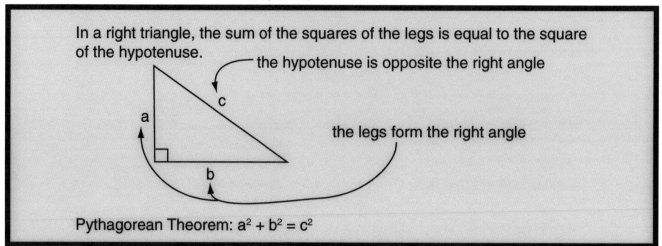

In a right triangle, the sum of the squares of the legs is equal to the square of the hypotenuse.

the hypotenuse is opposite the right angle

a

c

the legs form the right angle

b

Pythagorean Theorem: $a^2 + b^2 = c^2$

Solve for the missing side. Use the decoder to find out what the numbers 3, 6, 10, and 15 have in common.

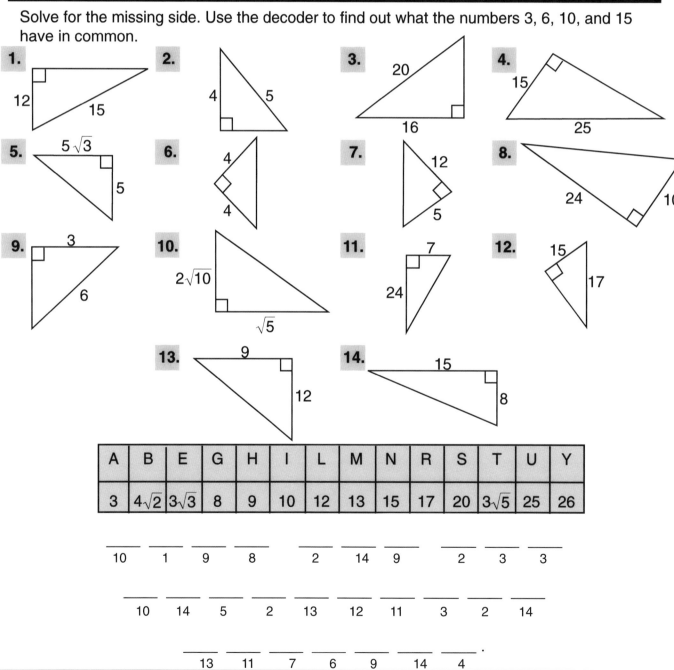

1.
12
15

2.
4
5

3.
20
16

4.
15
25

5.
$5\sqrt{3}$
5

6.
4
4

7.
12
5

8.
24
10

9.
3
6

10.
$2\sqrt{10}$
$\sqrt{5}$

11.
7
24

12.
15
17

13.
9
12

14.
15
8

A	B	E	G	H	I	L	M	N	R	S	T	U	Y
3	$4\sqrt{2}$	$3\sqrt{3}$	8	9	10	12	13	15	17	20	$3\sqrt{5}$	25	26

___ ___ ___ ___   ___ ___ ___   ___ ___ ___
10   1   9   8   2   14   9   2   3   3

___ ___ ___ ___ ___ ___ ___ ___ ___ ___
10 14   5   2   13 12 11   3   2   14

___ ___ ___ ___ ___ ___ ___ .
13 11   7   6   9   14   4

The Converse of the Pythagorean Theorem

The Pythagorean Theorem can be used to determine whether a triangle is ACUTE, RIGHT, or OBTUSE.

the triangle is:	if:
ACUTE	longest side^2 < short side^2 + other short side^2
RIGHT	longest side^2 = short side^2 + other short side^2
OBTUSE	longest side^2 > short side^2 + other short side^2

Determine whether the following lengths create an acute, right, obtuse, or no triangle. Check the corresponding column and place its letter in the blanks below to reveal Kirkpatrick Macmillan's invention.

	lengths	acute	right	obtuse	no triangle
1.	11, 11, 15	T	O	B	R
2.	1, 2, 3	A	N	E	H
3.	3, 4, 5	N	E	D	K
4.	7, 8, 12	L	R	B	P
5.	5, 12, 13	Z	I	Y	F
6.	6, 7, 8	C	D	I	A
7.	5, 9, 11	P	E	Y	N
8.	4, 5, 8	N	P	C	R
9.	9, 12, 15	S	L	E	O
10.	5, 5, 5	E	N	D	R

The Distance Formula

To find the length of a segment connecting two points (x_1, y_1) and (x_2, y_2) use the formula:

$$D = \sqrt{(x_2 - x_1)^2 + (y_2 - y_1)^2}$$

Example: Find the distance between (7, 2) and (4, 6).

Let (7, 2) be (x_1, y_1) and (4, 6) be (x_2, y_2);

then:
$$D = \sqrt{(4-7)^2 + (6-2)^2}$$
$$= \sqrt{(-3)^2 + (4)^2}$$
$$= \sqrt{9 + 16}$$
$$= \sqrt{25}$$
$$= 5 \text{ units}$$

Find the distance between the points listed. Use the results to find the distance from the pitcher's rubber to the home plate in baseball.

1. (−2, −3) and (−2, 4)

2. (−7, 5) and (1, −1)

3. (−2, 3) and (3, −2)

4. (−6, −2) and (−7, −5)

5. (−2, −1) and (−5, −5)

6. (−2, 6) and (−10, −9)

7. (2, −12) and (7, 0)

8. (3, −2) and (5, −3)

9. (−4, 5) and (8, −4)

10. (−3, 10) and (9, −6)

20	7	$\sqrt{5}$	13	15	5	$\sqrt{10}$	17	10	$5\sqrt{2}$
Y	C	E	F	H	I	N	S	T	X

$\overline{}\;\overline{}\;\overline{}\;\overline{}\;\overline{}\quad\overline{}\;\overline{}\;\overline{}\;\overline{}$,
6 5 3 2 10   7 8 8 2

$\overline{}\;\overline{}\;\overline{}\quad\overline{}\;\overline{}\;\overline{}\;\overline{}\;\overline{}\;\overline{}$
6 5 3   5 4 1 9 8 6

Names for Polygons

Match each polygon name with the correct number of sides.
Letters without lines through them will spell the answer.

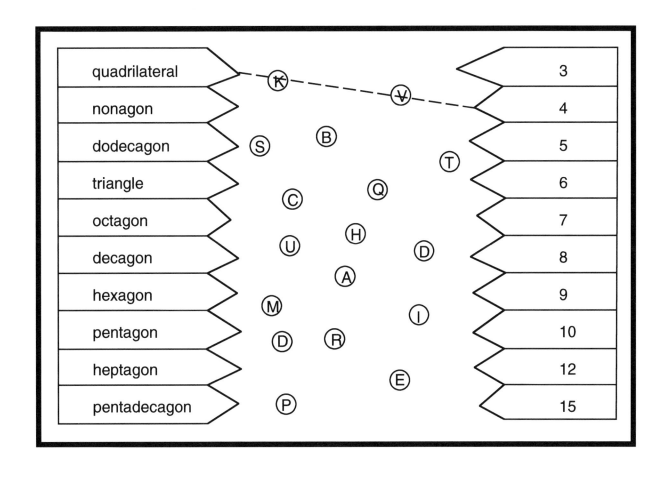

quadrilateral	3
nonagon	4
dodecagon	5
triangle	6
octagon	7
decagon	8
hexagon	9
pentagon	10
heptagon	12
pentadecagon	15

An equilateral, equiangular quadrilateral is called a

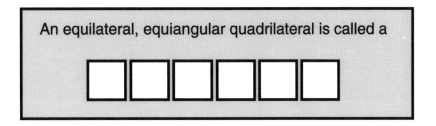

Interior Angle Sum of Convex Polygons

To find the total sum of the angles inside a convex polygon, divide the polygon into triangles by drawing all diagonals from one vertex. Count the number of triangles and multiply by _____°. (Hint: how many degrees are in a triangle?)

1.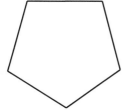

number of Δs _____
interior ∠ sum _____

2.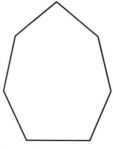

number of Δs _____
interior ∠ sum _____

3.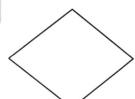

number of Δs _____
interior ∠ sum _____

4.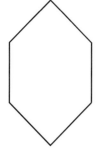

number of Δs _____
interior ∠ sum _____

5.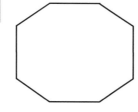

number of Δs _____
interior ∠ sum _____

6.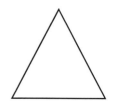

number of Δs _____
interior ∠ sum _____

Look for a pattern above. Compare the number of sides in the polygon to the number of triangles created. Use this pattern to determine the following:

7. interior ∠ sum of a decagon

8. interior ∠ sum of a dodecagon

9. interior ∠ sum of a 32–sided polygon

Angles in Regular Polygons

Follow these rules to find measures of angles in <u>regular</u> polygons:
number of triangles = number of sides − 2
interior angle sum = number of Δs • 180°
one interior angle = interior angle sum ÷ number of sides
exterior angle sum = 360°
one exterior angle = 360° ÷ number of sides

Solve for the indicated measure. Locate answers in the decoder to find the name of the man who patented the geodesic dome (a structure like the one at EPCOT center in Orlando, Florida). ALL POLYGONS REFERRED TO BELOW ARE REGULAR.

decoder

1. The measure of one interior angle of a hexagon.

2. The measure of one interior angle of a dodecagon.

3. The measure of one exterior angle of an octagon.

4. The measure of one exterior angle of a quadrilateral.

5. The interior angle sum of a pentagon.

6. The exterior angle sum of a 27–sided polygon.

7. The measure of one interior angle of a nonagon.

8. The measure of one exterior angle of a decagon.

9. The measure of one exterior angle of a dodecagon.

10. The measure of one interior angle of a triangle.

11. The measure of one interior angle of a pentagon.

12. The measure of one exterior angle of a nonagon.

13. The measure of one interior angle of an octagon.

Decoder	
360°	B
40°	C
140°	E
30°	F
135°	I
60°	K
120°	L
150°	M
108°	N
90°	R
36°	S
45°	T
540°	U

___. ___ ___ ___ ___ ___ ___ ___ ___ ___ ___ ___
 4   6   5   12 10   2   13 11   8   3   7   4

___ ___ ___ ___ ___ ___
 9   5   1   1   7   4

Review of Angles in Regular Polygons

Complete the missing angle measures in the chart below for the regular polygon named. If the polygon is not named, use the angle information to determine which polygon it is.

Remember: An interior ∠ and an exterior ∠ are supplementary.

	Polygon	Interior ∠ Sum	One Int. ∠	Exterior ∠ Sum	One Ext. ∠
1.	hexagon				
2.		540°			
3.			135°		
4.	decagon				
5.					30°
6.			90°		

Congruent Triangles

Three methods of proving triangles congruent:
Side–Side–Side (SSS)
> 3 sides of one triangle are congruent to 3 sides of another triangle.

Side–Angle–Side (SAS)
> 2 sides and the included angle of one triangle are congruent to 2 sides and the included angle of another triangle.

Angle–Side–Angle (ASA)
> 2 angles and the included side of one triangle are congruent to 2 angles and the included side of another triangle.

Use the diagrams and the information given to determine which of the above methods will prove the triangles congruent. Circle the letters beneath the correct method in the chart to reveal the mathematician who developed the symbol for congruence ($\cong$).

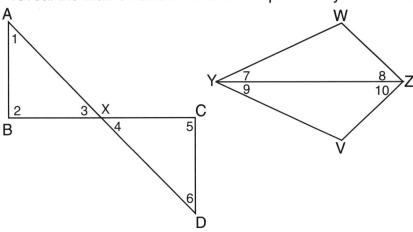

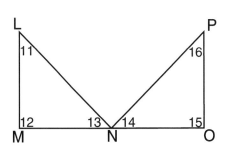

1. X is the midpoint of $\overline{AD}$ and $\overline{BC}$
2. $\overline{AB} \perp \overline{BC}$; $\overline{DC} \perp \overline{BC}$; BX = XC
3. $\overline{AB} \parallel \overline{CD}$; AB = CD
4. YW = YV; WZ = VZ
5. $\angle 7 = \angle 9$; $\angle 8 = \angle 10$
6. WZ = VZ; $\overline{YZ}$ bisects $\angle$WZV
7. $\overline{AD}$ and $\overline{BC}$ bisect each other
8. N is the midpoint of $\overline{MO}$; LM = PO; LN = PN
9. $\overline{LM}$ and $\overline{PO}$ are $\perp$ to $\overline{MO}$; $\angle 11 = \angle 16$; LM = PO
10. N is the midpoint of $\overline{MO}$; $\angle 12 = \angle 15$; $\angle 13 = \angle 14$
11. LM = PO; MN = NO; LN = PN
12. $\overline{ZY}$ bisects $\angle$WYV; WY = YV
13. $\angle 1 = \angle 6$; X is the midpoint of $\overline{AD}$
14. N is the midpoint of $\overline{MO}$; LN = PN; $\angle 13 = \angle 14$
15. $\overline{YZ}$ bisects $\angle$WYV and $\angle$WZV
16. $\triangle$WYZ and $\triangle$VYZ are equilateral

	SSS	SAS	ASA
1.	A	G	R
2.	C	H	O
3.	I	M	T
4.	T	E	D
5.	E	S	F
6.	T	R	H
7.	A	I	L
8.	E	Z	P
9.	L	M	D
10.	B	P	L
11.	E	A	S
12.	C	I	A
13.	L	O	B
14.	Q	N	P
15.	R	M	I
16.	Z	O	S

___ ___ ___ ___ ___ ___ ___ ___

___ ___ ___ ___ ___ ___ ___

Additional Congruence Methods

Angle–Angle–Side : (AAS)	Two angles and a non–included side of one triangle congruent to two angles and a non–included side of another triangle.
Hypotenuse–Leg : (HL)	In a right triangle, the hypotenuse and one leg congruent to the hypotenuse and leg of another right triangle.

In the chart, place an X in <u>all</u> columns that can be applied to prove the triangles congruent. The remaining letters will reveal what Whitcomb L. Judson did in Chicago in 1893.

1.

2.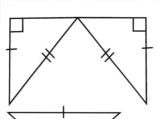

3.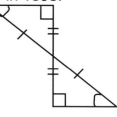

4.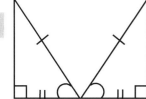

5.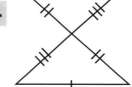

6.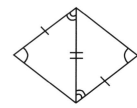

7.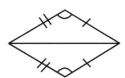

8.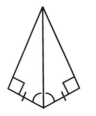

9.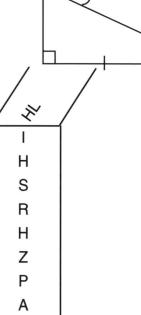

	SSS	SAS	ASA	AAS	HL
1.	A	S	H	E	I
2.	N	V	E	N	H
3.	T	E	W	A	S
4.	E	A	F	I	R
5.	E	M	D	T	H
6.	E	N	E	Z	Z
7.	I	O	I	P	P
8.	E	B	O	Y	A
9.	R	F	A	I	Q

___ ___ ___   ___ ___ ___ ___

___ ___ ___ ___   ___ ___ ___ ___ ___ ___

Operations With Radical Expressions

⇒ Like radicals add and subtract in the same manner as like terms in algebra:

$$3x + 2x = 5x \qquad\qquad 7y - 3y = 4y$$
$$3\sqrt{2} + 2\sqrt{2} = 5\sqrt{2} \qquad 7\sqrt{5} - 3\sqrt{5} = 4\sqrt{5}$$

⇒ Distribute the values outside of the parentheses:

$$3\,(2x + 7) \qquad \text{simplifies to} \qquad 6x + 21$$

$$4\sqrt{3}\,(2\sqrt{2} - 5) \qquad \text{simplifies to} \qquad 8\sqrt{6} - 20\sqrt{3}$$

⇒ To rationalize the denominator, multiply both numerator and denominator by the radical being eliminated. Then simplify:

$$\frac{8\sqrt{3}}{\sqrt{2}} \cdot \frac{\sqrt{2}}{\sqrt{2}} = \frac{8\sqrt{6}}{\sqrt{4}} = \frac{8\sqrt{6}}{2} = 4\sqrt{6}$$

Remember: In fractions, reduce whole numbers with whole numbers and radicals with radicals—never mix!

Simplify the radical expressions completely. Use the decoder to reveal the first civilization to compute with radicals.

1. $4\sqrt{3} + 7\sqrt{3}$

2. $7\left(8\sqrt{3} + 2\sqrt{2}\right)$

3. $5\sqrt{2}\left(3 - 2\sqrt{2}\right)$

4. $10\sqrt{2} - 2\sqrt{8}$

5. $\sqrt{10} \bullet \sqrt{5}$

6. $\sqrt{75}$

7. $\sqrt{121}$

8. $4\sqrt{2} + 7\sqrt{2} - 3\sqrt{2}$

9. $\sqrt{6} \bullet \sqrt{15}$

10. $\sqrt{\frac{4}{9}}$

11. $\frac{5}{\sqrt{10}}$

12. $\frac{2\sqrt{3}}{\sqrt{6}}$

13. $\frac{1}{\sqrt{2}}$

14. $\frac{5}{\sqrt{75}}$

$5\sqrt{2}$	$3\sqrt{10}$	$\frac{2}{3}$	$6\sqrt{2}$	$\frac{\sqrt{10}}{2}$	$15\sqrt{2}-20$	11	$5\sqrt{3}$	$\sqrt{2}$	$11\sqrt{3}$	$8\sqrt{2}$	$\frac{\sqrt{2}}{2}$	$\frac{\sqrt{3}}{3}$	$56\sqrt{3}+14\sqrt{2}$
E	B	T	A	N	H	A	B	Y	I	N	L	S	O

$\overline{}$ $\overline{}$ $\overline{}$ $\quad$ $\overline{}$ $\overline{}$ $\overline{}$ $\overline{}$ $\overline{}$ $\overline{}$ $\overline{}$ $\overline{}$ $\overline{}$ $\overline{}$

10 $\quad$ 3 $\quad$ 5 $\qquad$ 9 $\quad$ 7 $\quad$ 6 $\quad$ 12 $\quad$ 13 $\quad$ 2 $\quad$ 8 $\quad$ 1 $\quad$ 4 $\quad$ 11 $\quad$ 14

Special Right Triangles

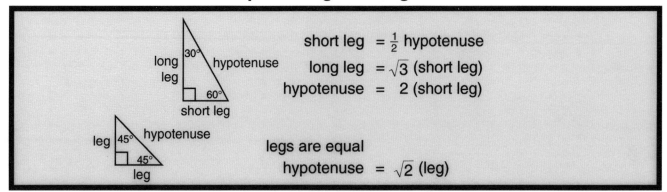

short leg = $\frac{1}{2}$ hypotenuse

long leg = $\sqrt{3}$ (short leg)

hypotenuse = 2 (short leg)

legs are equal

hypotenuse = $\sqrt{2}$ (leg)

Use the 30–60–90 and 45–45–90 triangle relationships to solve for the missing sides. Use the answers to reveal the name of the team that Abraham M. Saperstein established and sent on the road in 1927.

1.

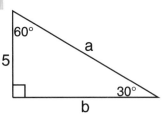

2.

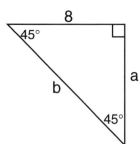

3.

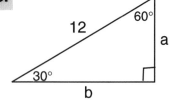

4.

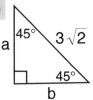

5.

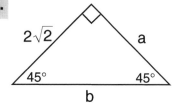

6.

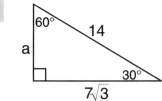

7.

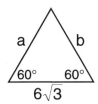

8.

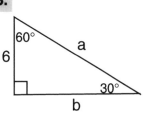

9.

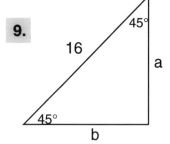

8	$2\sqrt{2}$	3	6	$5\sqrt{3}$	4	7	12	$8\sqrt{2}$	10	$6\sqrt{3}$
A	B	E	G	H	L	M	O	R	S	T

___ ___ ___ ___ ___ ___ ___ ___ ___
8b 1b 4a 1b 2a 9b 5b 4b 6a

___ ___ ___ ___ ___ ___ ___ ___ ___ ___ ___ ___ ___
3a 5b 8a 5a 4a 7a 2b 8a 7b 3b 4b 9a 1a

Properties of Parallelograms

Parallelograms have all of these properties:
—both pairs of opposite sides parallel
—both pairs of opposite sides congruent
—both pairs of opposite angles congruent
—diagonals bisect each other

Shade the answers below to discover the corporation whose success is based on the invention of Chester Carlson.

1. If CA = 10, EK = _____ .

2. If CK = 18, CX = _____ .

3. If ∠CEK = 85°, ∠CAK = _____ .

4. If ∠ECA = 130°, ∠CAK = _____ .

5. If ∠1 = 40° and ∠2 = 65°, ∠EKA = _____ .

6. If EX = 15, EA = _____ .

7. If CE = 12, KA = _____ .

8. If ∠8 = 25° and ∠7 = 35°, ∠EKA = _____ .

9. If CX = 5x − 44 and XK = 2x + 25, then x = _____ .

10. If ∠7 = 30° and ∠4 = 40°, ∠EKA = _____ .

11. If CE = 3x + 5 and AK = 7x − 15, then x = _____ .

12. If ∠ECA = 6x − 20 and ∠EKA = 2x + 80, then x = _____ .

13. If ∠CAE = 35°, ∠AEK = _____ .

14. If ∠2 = 100° and ∠3 = 20°, ∠CXA = _____ .

15. If ∠CEK = 80°, ∠EKA = _____ .

16. ∠1 + ∠2 + ∠3 + ∠4 + ∠5 + ∠6 + ∠7 + ∠8 = _____ .

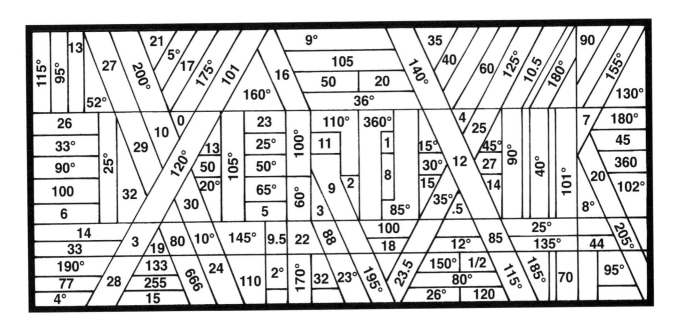

Properties of the Rectangle, Rhombus, and Square

Rectangle	**Rhombus**
all properties of parallelograms plus	all properties of parallelograms plus
—all diagonals are congruent	—all sides are congruent
—all angles measure 90°	—all diagonals are perpendicular
	—all diagonals bisect opposite angles

Square
all properties of
—parallelogram
—rectangle
—rhombus

Use the properties to solve for the missing measures in the diagrams.

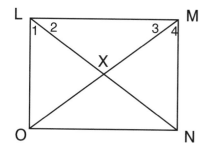

1. LMNO is a rectangle. If LM = 16, MN = 12, and ∠1 = 60°, find the following:
   - a. ON = _____
   - b. OL = _____
   - c. LN = _____
   - d. LX = _____
   - e. ∠LON = _____
   - f. ∠2 = _____
   - g. OX = _____
   - h. ∠3 = _____
   - i. ∠4 = _____

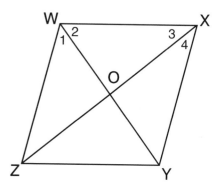

2. WXYZ is a rhombus. If WX = 4 and ∠WXY = 60°, find the following:
   - a. XY = _____
   - b. ∠ZWX = _____
   - c. ∠1 = _____
   - d. ∠2 = _____
   - e. ∠3 = _____
   - f. ∠4 = _____
   - g. WO = _____
   - h. OX = _____
   - i. WY = _____

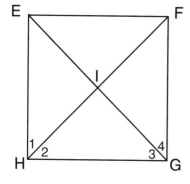

3. EFGH is a square. If EF = 10, find the following:
   - a. FG = _____
   - b. ∠EFG = _____
   - c. EG = _____
   - d. EI = _____
   - e. IF = _____
   - f. ∠EIF = _____
   - g. ∠1 = _____
   - h. ∠3 = _____
   - i. HF = _____

Trapezoids

All trapezoids have exactly one pair of parallel sides (called bases).
An isosceles trapezoid has congruent legs, base angles, and diagonals.
A right trapezoid has two right angles.

Any trapezoid can be divided into a rectangle and triangle(s) by drawing altitudes between the bases. This will aid in finding measures of segments and angles.

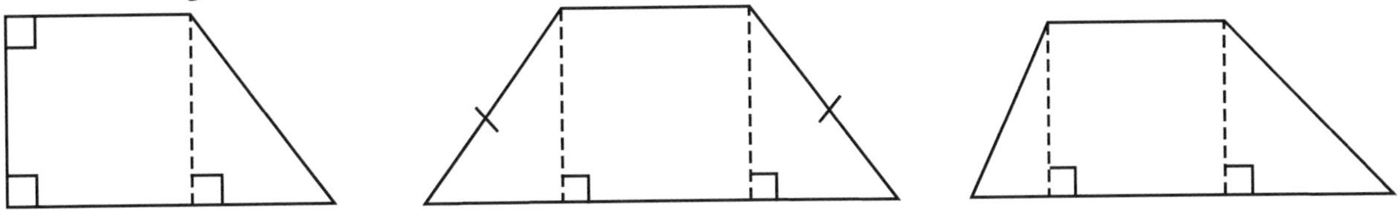

right trapezoid   isosceles trapezoid   general trapezoid

Use the properties of trapezoids, rectangles, and right triangles to find the missing measures. Shade the answers below to find which U.S. state has borders that closely resemble a right trapezoid.

1.
4 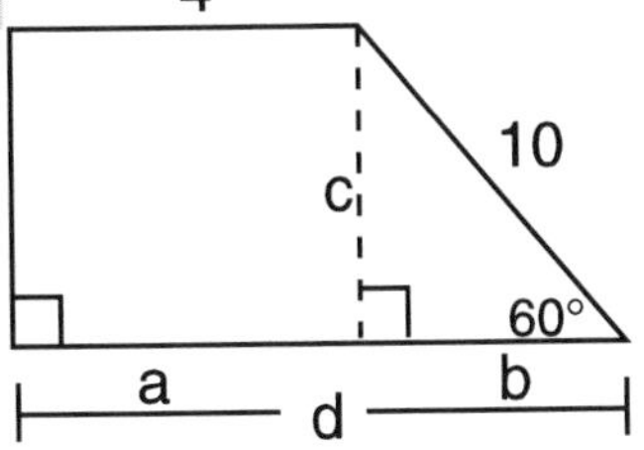
10
c
60°
a
d
b

2.
12 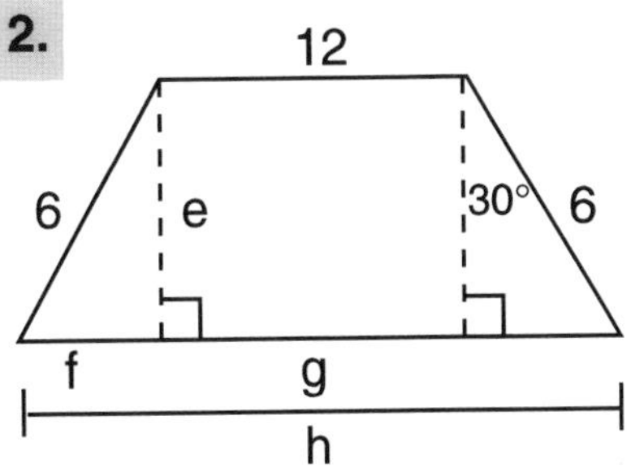
6
e
30°
6
f
g
h

3.
8 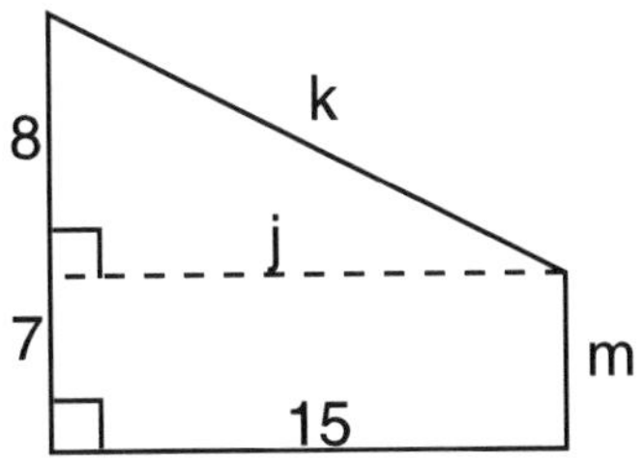
k
j
7
15
m

4.
r 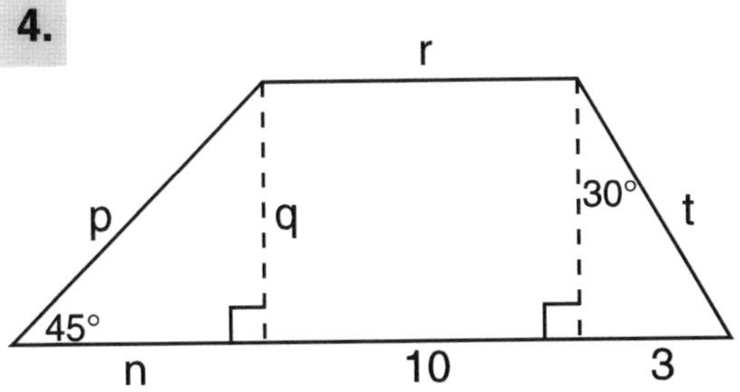
p
q
30°
t
45°
n
10
3

5.
w
12
x
20
u
v
10

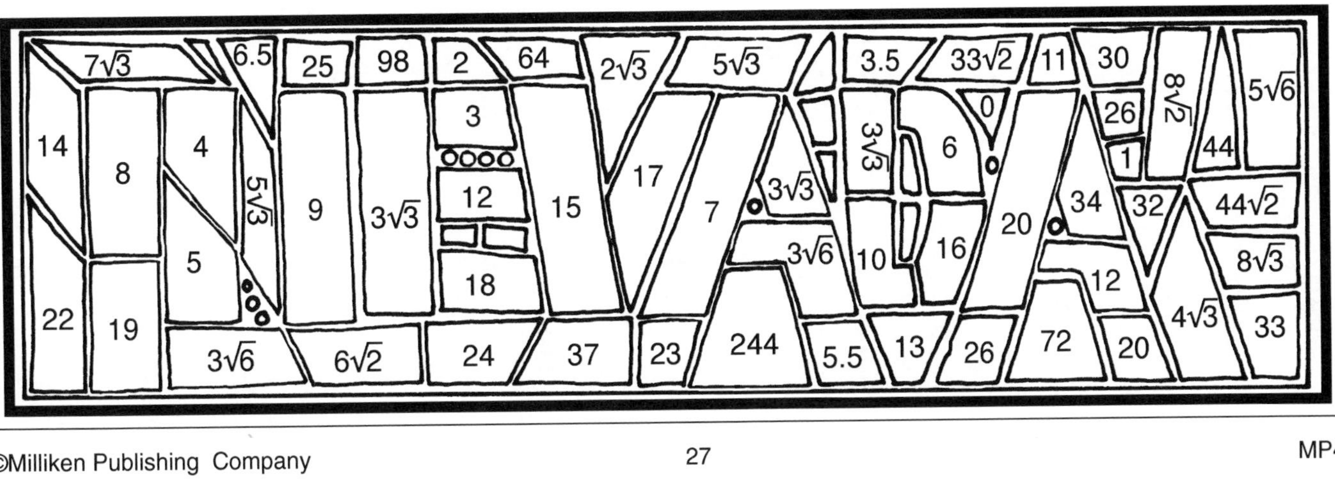

$7\sqrt{3}$ 6.5 25 98 2 64 $2\sqrt{3}$ $5\sqrt{3}$ 3.5 $33\sqrt{2}$ 11 30 $8\sqrt{2}$ $5\sqrt{6}$
14 8 4 3 0 26 44
$5\sqrt{3}$ $3\sqrt{3}$ 6 1 $44\sqrt{2}$
9 $3\sqrt{3}$ 12 15 17 7 $3\sqrt{3}$ 20 34 32 $8\sqrt{3}$
5 0000 $3\sqrt{6}$ 10 16 12
18 20
22 19
$3\sqrt{6}$ $6\sqrt{2}$ 24 37 23 244 5.5 13 26 72 20 $4\sqrt{3}$ 33

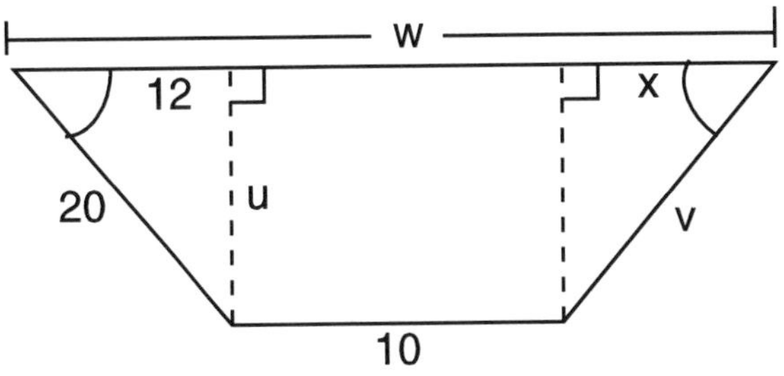

Quadrilateral Review

1. A parallelogram is _____ a quadrilateral.

2. A rectangle is _____ a trapezoid.

3. A rhombus is _____ a parallelogram.

4. A square is _____ a quadrilateral.

5. A rectangle is _____ a rhombus.

6. A rhombus is _____ a square.

7. A trapezoid is _____ isosceles.

8. A rectangle is _____ a square.

9. A square is _____ a rectangle.

10. A trapezoid is _____ a parallelogram.

11. A rectangle _____ has four right angles.

12. A rhombus _____ has four right angles.

13. A quadrilateral is _____ a pentagon.

14. A parallelogram is _____ equilateral.

15. A trapezoid is _____ equilateral.

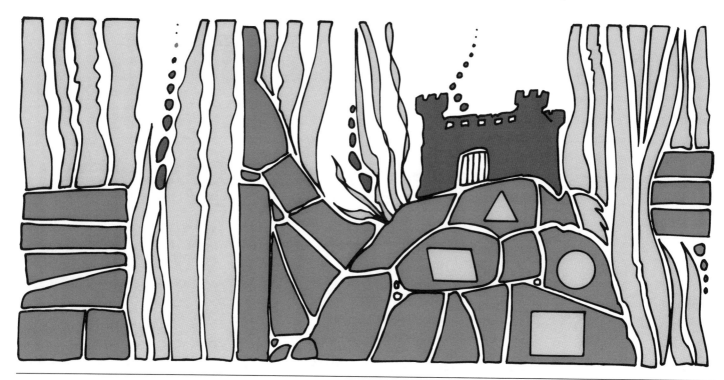

Perimeter

Perimeter is the total distance around a figure. Add the lengths of the segments that outline the figure to find its perimeter. Perimeter is measured in linear units (inches, centimeters, feet, and so on).

Find the perimeter of each figure. Place your answers in the cross–number puzzle below.

ACROSS
1. An equilateral triangle with sides of 6 cm.
2. A regular dodecagon with sides of 5 cm.
3. A regular hexagon with sides of 12 in.
4. A square whose diagonal measures $2\sqrt{2}$ mm.
5. A regular pentagon with sides of 8 ft.
6. A rectangle whose diagonal and side measure 13 cm and 5 cm, respectively.
9. An octagon with sides of 7 m.
10. A decagon with sides of 5 cm.

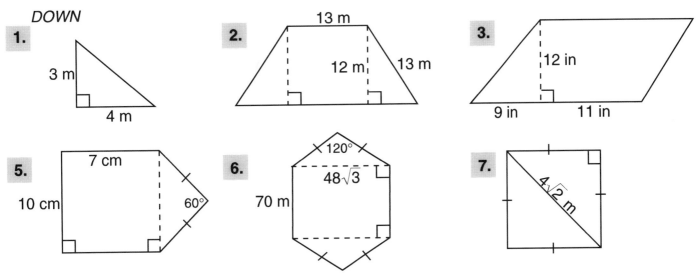

DOWN

8. A regular decagon with sides of 15 in.
9. A right trapezoid whose parallel sides measure 9 m and 17 m, and the distance between them is 15 m.

Area of Triangles, Parallelograms, and Trapezoids

Area of any parallelogram: A = base x height
Remember: Height is perpendicular to the base.

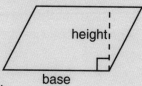

Area of any triangle: $A = \frac{1}{2}$ (base x height)

Area of any trapezoid: $A = \frac{1}{2}$ height (base$_1$ + base$_2$)
Alternatively, divide the trapezoid into rectangles and triangles and add the areas together.

Find the area of the shapes. Then use a ruler to match the problem number with the area in the puzzle. The letters that remain will reveal the U.S. state that borders only one other state.

1.
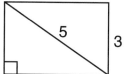

2.
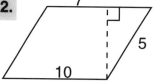

3.

4.
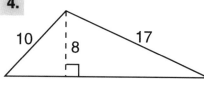

5.
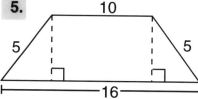

6.
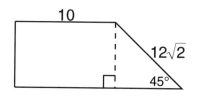

7. A 30–60–90 triangle with short leg measuring 6 units.
8. A square whose perimeter is 36 units.
9. A square whose diagonal measures 8 units.
10. A triangle with sides of 3, 4, and 5 units.

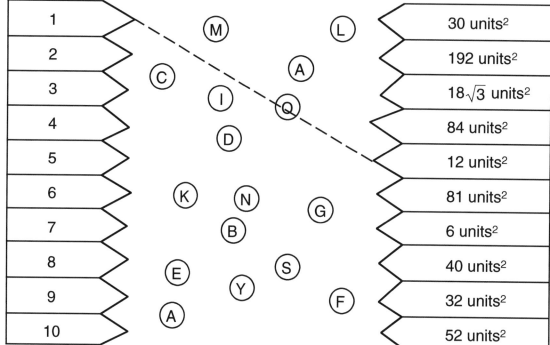

1	30 units²
2	192 units²
3	18√3 units²
4	84 units²
5	12 units²
6	81 units²
7	6 units²
8	40 units²
9	32 units²
10	52 units²

Circumference and Area of Circles

Circumference is the distance around a circle. Think of it as the circle's perimeter. Find circumference by multiplying the diameter (or twice the length of the radius) by π:

$$C = \pi d \qquad OR \qquad C = 2\pi r$$

Area of a circle is found by squaring the length of the radius and then multiplying by π:

$$A = \pi r^2$$

Match the radius with the correct circumference and area. The remaining letters will reveal the inventor of bifocals.

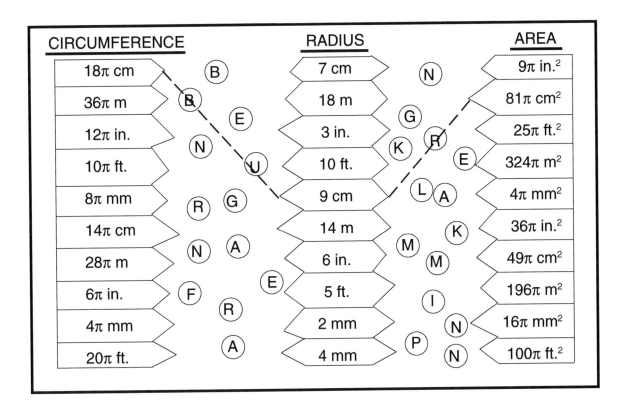

CIRCUMFERENCE	RADIUS	AREA
18π cm (B)	7 cm (N)	9π in.²
36π m (B)	18 m (G)	81π cm²
12π in. (E)	3 in. (K) (R)	25π ft.²
10π ft. (N) (U)	10 ft. (E)	324π m²
8π mm (R) (G)	9 cm (L) (A)	4π mm²
14π cm	14 m (K)	36π in.²
28π m (N) (A)	6 in. (M) (M)	49π cm²
6π in. (F) (E)	5 ft. (I)	196π m²
4π mm (R)	2 mm (N)	16π mm²
20π ft. (A)	4 mm (P) (N)	100π ft.²

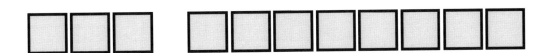

Surface Area of Right Prisms and Cylinders

To find total surface area of any solid, find the areas of the polygons that form the solid. Then add the areas together.

<u>Right Prisms</u>

Right prisms have two congruent bases which lie in parallel planes. The lateral faces of a right prism are rectangles. The prism is named by the shape of its base.

Example:
Triangular Prism

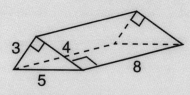

Area of triangular base = $\frac{1}{2}$ (3 x 4) = 6
Area of lateral faces = 4 x 8 = 32
                        3 x 8 = 24
                        5 x 8 = 40
Add two bases to lateral faces $\Rightarrow$
2 (6) + 32 + 24 + 40 =
        12 + 96 = 108 square units

<u>Cylinders</u>

Cylinders have two congruent circles for bases. The lateral surface is one large rectangle whose dimensions are formed by the height of the cylinder and the circumference of the base (think of the label on a can).
Example:

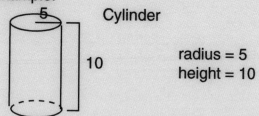

Cylinder

radius = 5
height = 10

Area of circular base = π (5)^2 = 25π
Area of lateral surface = circumference x height
                    2π (5) x 10 =
                    10π x 10 = 100π
Add two bases to lateral surface $\Rightarrow$
        2 (25π) + 100π =
        50π + 100π = 150π square units

Find the total surface area of the solids below.

1. Cylinder with radius 5 ft. and height 8 ft.
2. Cylinder with radius 3 ft. and height 10 ft.
3. Cylinder with diameter of 20 mm and height 12 mm.
4. Cylinder with diameter of 10 in. and height 5 in.

5. Cube with edge of 7 mm.
6. Cube with edge of 9 in.
7. Rectangular prism with length 5 mm, width 6 mm, and height 8 mm.
8. Rectangular prism with length 8 cm, width 10 cm, and height 12 cm.

9.   **10.**   **11.**

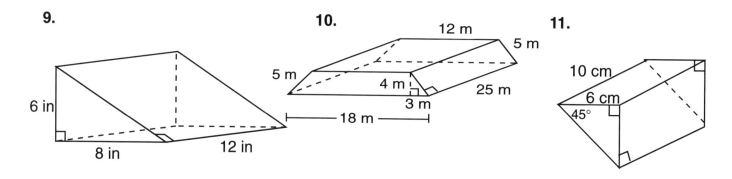

Volume of Right Prisms and Cylinders

Volume of right prisms and cylinders is found by multiplying the area of the base by the height of the solid.
Remember: The bases are parallel faces of the solid.

Find the volume of the solids, then use the answers to reveal the inventor of a famous beverage.

1. Triangular right prism whose base is an equilateral triangle with sides of 10 cm; height of prism is 15 cm.
2. Cube whose edges are 12 mm.
3. Rectangular prism with length 6 cm, width 5 cm, and height 10 cm.
4. Triangular right prism whose base is a right triangle with sides of 3 cm, 4 cm, and 5 cm; height of prism is 12 cm.
5. Rectangular prism with length 8 mm, width 10 mm, and height 15 mm.
6. Cylinder with radius of 10 cm and height of 12 cm.
7. Cylinder with radius of 15 mm and height of 25 mm.
8. Cylinder with diameter of 18 cm and height of 5 cm.
9. Cylinder with diameter of 10 mm and height of 30 mm.
10. Cylinder with radius 6 cm and height of 10 cm.
11. Cylinder with diameter 20 mm and height of 15 mm.

12.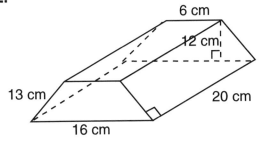

13.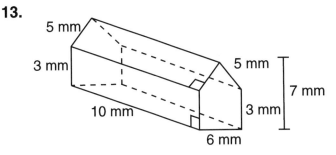

14.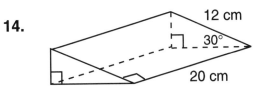

1200 mm³	1500π mm³	300 cm³	5625π mm³	1200π cm³	375√3 cm³	2640 cm³
A	B	C	E	H	J	L
72 cm³	240 mm³	405π cm³	360√3 cm³	1728 mm³	360π cm³	750π mm³
M	N	O	P	R	S	T

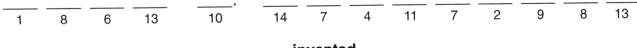

___ ___ ___ ___ ___ . ___ ___ ___ ___ ___ ___ ___ ___
 1   8   6   13   10   14   7   4   11   7   2   9   8   13

invented

___ ___ ___ ___   ___ ___ ___ ___ .
 3   8   3   5   3   8   12   5

Surface Area of Regular Right Pyramids and Cones

To find total surface area, add the areas of all polygons forming the solid.

Regular Right Pyramids

A regular right pyramid has a regular polygon for its base and congruent isosceles triangles for lateral faces. The slant height (colored line below) must be used to find the area of these triangles.

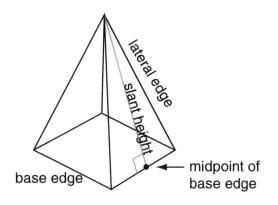

lateral edge

slant height

base edge

midpoint of base edge

Cones

A cone has a circle for a base and a triangular sector for its lateral face. The circumference of the base and the slant height are used to find the area of this sector.

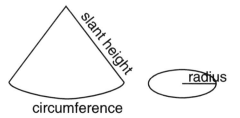

slant height

radius

circumference

Area of Lateral Surface

$A = \frac{1}{2}$ base $\cdot$ height

$A = \frac{1}{2}$ circumference $\cdot$ slant height

Area of Base

$A = \pi r^2$

Add together to find the total surface area.

Find the total surface area of the square pyramids and cones below. Use the answers to reveal an interesting geographical fact.

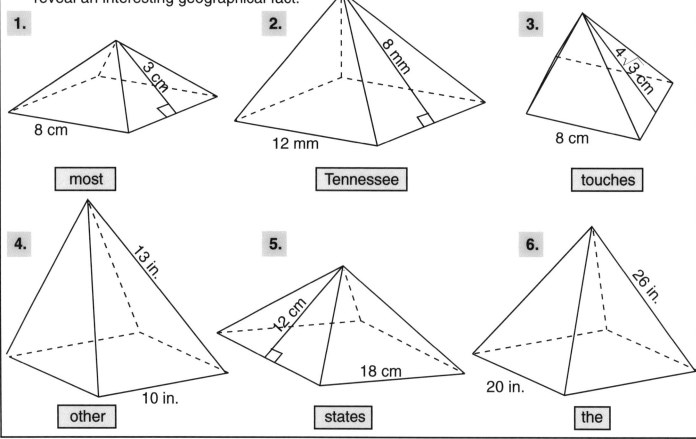

1.

3 cm

8 cm

most

2.

8 mm

12 mm

Tennessee

3.

$4\sqrt{3}$ cm

8 cm

touches

4.

13 in.

10 in.

other

5.

12 cm

18 cm

states

6.

26 in.

20 in.

the

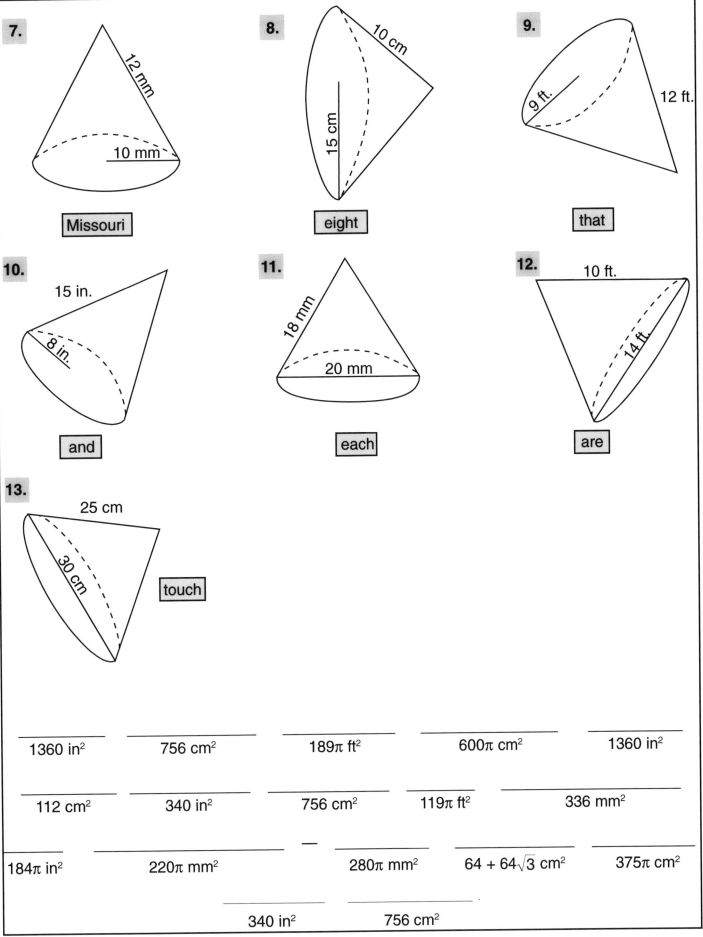

7. 12 mm 10 mm

Missouri

8. 10 cm 15 cm

eight

9. 9 ft. 12 ft.

that

10. 15 in. 8 in.

and

11. 18 mm 20 mm

each

12. 10 ft. 14 ft.

are

13. 25 cm 30 cm

touch

1360 in²	756 cm²	189π ft²	600π cm²	1360 in²
112 cm²	340 in²	756 cm²	119π ft²	336 mm²
184π in²	220π mm²	280π mm²	64 + 64√3 cm²	375π cm²
	340 in²	756 cm²		

Volume of Regular Right Pyramids and Cones

To find the volume of either of these solids, use this formula:

$$\text{Volume} = \frac{1}{3}(\text{Area of base})(\text{altitude of the solid})$$

Pyramids
The base is a regular polygon; the altitude is the distance from the center of the base to the vertex (tip) of the pyramid.

Cones
The base is a circle; the altitude is the distance from the center of the circle to the vertex (tip) of the cone.

Notice the right triangle formed in each of these solids. Use this triangle and the Pythagorean theorem to solve for needed measures when they are not given.

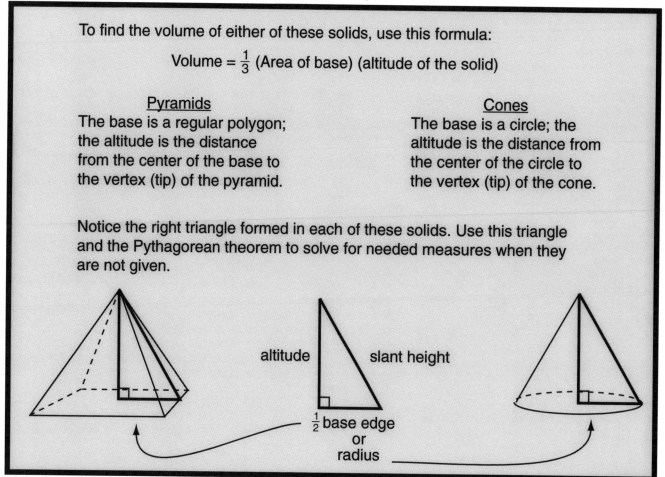

altitude   slant height

$\frac{1}{2}$ base edge
or
radius

Find the volume of the solids described below. Use the decoder to reveal the name of the first woman to appear on a U.S. postage stamp.

1. Regular square pyramid with base edge 8 cm and altitude 12 cm.
2. Cone with radius 6 cm and altitude 8 cm.
3. Regular square pyramid with base edge 5 m and altitude 3 m.
4. Cone with radius 10 m and altitude 9 m.
5. Regular square pyramid with base edge 3 in. and altitude 5 in.
6. Cone with diameter 16 in. and altitude 6 in.
7. Regular square pyramid with base edge 12 cm and slant height 10 cm.
8. Cone with radius 15 mm and slant height 30 mm.
9. Regular square pyramid with altitude 20 mm and slant height 25 mm.
10. Cone with altitude 10 ft. and slant height 26 ft.
11. Regular <u>triangular</u> pyramid with base edge 8 cm and altitude 12 cm.

1920π ft³	300π m³	15 in.³	6000 mm³	$1125\pi\sqrt{3}$ mm³	128π in.³	$64\sqrt{3}$ cm³	384 cm³	25 m³	256 cm³	96π cm³
A	G	H	I	M	N	O	R	S	T	W

 ___ ___ ___ ___ ___ ___   ___ ___ ___   ___ ___ ___ ___ ___ ___
  8   10   7   1   5   10   2   10   3   5   9   6   4   1   11   6

MP4057

Volume of Combination Solids

Find the volume of individual solids and then add the results to find the total volume of combination solids. Use the formulas below.

Volume of any right prism: (area of base) (height)

Volume of regular pyramid: $\frac{1}{3}$ (area of base) (altitude)

Volume of cylinder: $\pi r^2 h$

Volume of cone: $\frac{1}{3} \pi r^2$ (altitude)

Remember: The altitude is the length from the tip (vertex) to the center of the base.

Find the volume of the solids below to reveal the name of the ancient unit which measured the distance from the elbow to the tip of the middle finger.

1. a = 3 cm, b = 4 cm, h = 7 cm
2. a = 3 cm, b = 6 cm, h = 10 cm
3. a = 4 cm, b = 6 cm, h = 14 cm
4. a = 6 cm, b = 10 cm, h = 8 cm

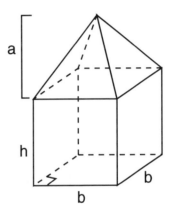

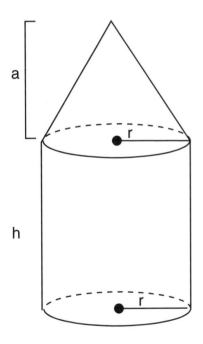

5. a = 9 cm, r = 4 cm, h = 10 cm
6. a = 12 cm, r = 8 cm, h = 4 cm
7. a = 6 cm, r = 6 cm, h = 14 cm

512π	396	208π	1000	128	576π	552
B	C	E	H	I	T	U

___ ___ ___ ___ ___ ___ ___ ___
7   4   5   2   3   6   1   7

Circle Terminology

Write the term in the blanks beside the definition. The circled letters will reveal the meaning of "E Pluribus Unum."

1. segment joining two points on a circle   __ __ Ⓞ __ __

2. distance around a circle   __ __ __ __ __ __ __ __ Ⓞ __ Ⓞ

3. circles with the same center   __ Ⓞ __ __ __ __ __ __ __ __

4. segment from the center to a point on the circle   __ __ __ __ Ⓞ __

5. line intersecting a circle in two points   __ __ __ __ __ Ⓞ

6. arc measuring less than 180°   __ __ __ Ⓞ __ **arc**

7. A semicircle is _____ of a circle.   __ __ __ Ⓞ

8. longest chord   __ __ __ Ⓞ __ __ __ __

9. arc measuring more than 180°   __ Ⓞ __ __ __ **arc**

10. angle formed by two radii   __ __ Ⓞ __ __ __ __ **angle**

11. The place where a tangent line intersects a circle.   __ __ __ __ __ __ **of**

   __ __ __ __ __ __ __ Ⓞ

☐☐☐   ☐☐☐   ☐☐   ☐☐☐☐

©Milliken Publishing Company   38   MP4057

Arcs, Central Angles, and Inscribed Angles

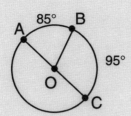

minor arc : $\overset{\frown}{AB}$
major arc : $\overset{\frown}{ACB}$
semicircle : $\overset{\frown}{AC}$

$\angle AOB = \overset{\frown}{AB} = 85°$
$\angle BOC = \overset{\frown}{BC} = 95°$

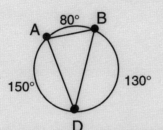

$\angle ADB = \frac{1}{2}\overset{\frown}{AB} = \frac{1}{2}(80°) = 40°$
$\angle DAB = \frac{1}{2}\overset{\frown}{BD} = \frac{1}{2}(130°) = 65°$
$\angle ABD = \frac{1}{2}\overset{\frown}{AD} = \frac{1}{2}(150°) = 75°$

(notice: the angles of $\triangle ABD$ add to _____°)

1. $\overset{\frown}{WX}$ = _____ °
2. $\angle XOY$ = _____ °
3. $\overset{\frown}{VY}$ = _____ °
4. $\overset{\frown}{XV}$ = _____ °
5. $\angle WZY$ = _____ °

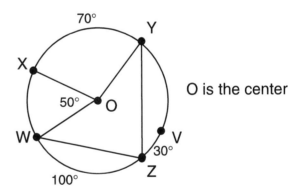

O is the center

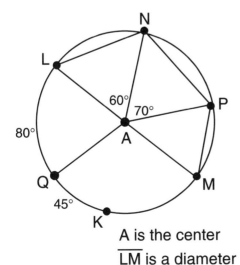

A is the center
$\overline{LM}$ is a diameter

6. $\overset{\frown}{LN}$ = _____ °
7. $\angle MAP$ = _____ °
8. $\overset{\frown}{NP}$ = _____ °
9. $\overset{\frown}{KM}$ = _____ °
10. $\angle QAM$ = _____ °
11. $\angle LMP$ = _____ °
12. $\angle MLN$ = _____ °
13. $\angle LNA$ = _____ °
14. $\angle PAQ$ = _____ °
15. $\angle QAL$ = _____ °
16. $\overset{\frown}{KLN}$ = _____ °

Angles Formed by Chords, Secants, and Tangents

Angles formed by chords: Add two intercepted arcs and divide by two.

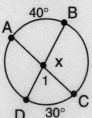

to find the measure of $\angle 1$:

$$\frac{\overarc{AB} + \overarc{CD}}{2} = \frac{40 + 30}{2} = \frac{70}{2} = 35°$$

Angles formed by secants and tangents: Subtract smaller intercepted arc from larger intercepted arc and divide by two.

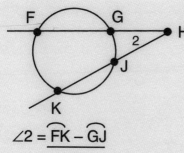

$$\angle 2 = \frac{\overarc{FK} - \overarc{GJ}}{2}$$

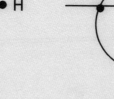

$$\angle 3 = \frac{\overarc{LP} - \overarc{MP}}{2}$$

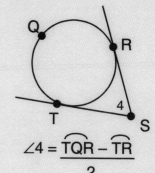

$$\angle 4 = \frac{\overarc{TQR} - \overarc{TR}}{2}$$

Remember: angles INSIDE   : ADD arcs and divide by 2
angles OUTSIDE   : SUBTRACT arcs and divide by 2

Use the diagrams above and the information given to find the missing measures. Use the decoder to reveal the basketball player who scored 100 points in a game on March 2, 1962.

1. $\overarc{AB} = 60°$, $\overarc{DC} = 50°$, $\angle 1 =$ _____°

2. $\overarc{AB} = 50°$, $\overarc{AD} = 160°$, $\overarc{BC} = 120°$, $\angle 1 =$ _____°

3. $\overarc{AD} = 50°$, $\overarc{DC} = 25°$, $\overarc{CB} = 140°$, $\angle 1 =$ _____°

4. $\overarc{FK} = 75°$, $\overarc{GJ} = 25°$, $\angle 2 =$ _____°

5. $\overarc{FG} = 120°$, $\overarc{GJ} = 40°$, $\overarc{JK} = 100°$, $\angle 2 =$ _____°

6. $\overarc{FK} = 110°$, $\overarc{KJ} = 90°$, $\overarc{FG} = 120°$, $\angle 2 =$ _____°

7. $\overarc{LP} = 145°$, $\overarc{MP} = 45°$, $\angle 3 =$ _____°

8. $\overarc{LM} = 90°$, $\overarc{MP} = 90°$, $\angle 3 =$ _____°

9. $\overarc{LM} = 100°$, $\overarc{LP} = 210°$, $\angle 3 =$ _____°

10. $\overarc{QT} = 120°$, $\overarc{QR} = 130°$, $\angle 4 =$ _____°

11. $\overarc{QR} = 155°$, $\overarc{TR} = 115°$, $\angle 4 =$ _____°

12. $\overarc{QT} = 125°$, $\overarc{TR} = 85°$, $\angle 4 =$ _____°

A	B	C	E	H	I	L	M	N	R	T	W
30°	85°	80°	70°	55°	50°	35°	40°	65°	45°	95°	25°

___ ___ ___ ___   ___ ___ ___ ___ ___ ___ ___ ___   ___ ___ ___
4   7   6   12   9   1   5   2   3   10 8   6   5   7   11

Length of Chords

If two chords intersect, the product of the segments along one chord is equal to the product of the segments along the other chord.

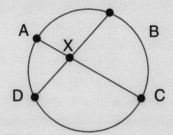

$$(AX)\,(XC) = (DX)\,(XB)$$

Use the diagram above and the measures given to find the missing lengths.

1. AX = 3, XC = 4, DX = 6; find XB, AC, and DB.

2. DX = 5, XB = 8, AX = 10; find XC, AC, and DB.

3. XB = 7, DX = 8, AX = 14; find XC, AC, and DB.

4. AX = 9, XC = 4, DX = 12; find XB, AC, and DB.

5. DX = 4, XB = 12, AX = 6; find XC, AC, and DB.

6. XB = 6, DX = 12, AX = 9; find XC, AC, and DB.

7. AX = 9, XC = 16, DX = BX; find DX, XB, AC, and DB.

8. DX = 5, XB = 20, AX = XC; find AX, XC, AC, and DB.

9. XB = 10, DB = 16, AX = 12; find XC, AC, and DX.

10. AC = 14, AX = 2, DX = 3; find XB, DB, and XC.

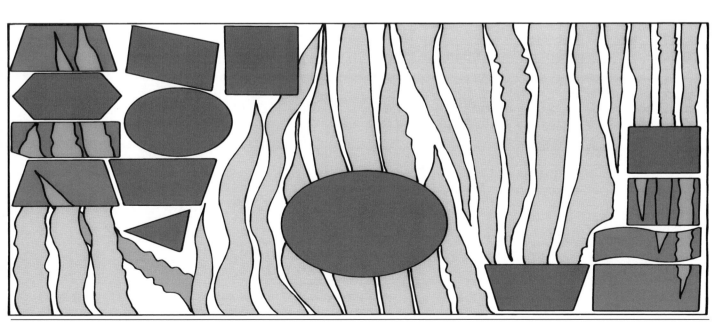

Length of Secant and Tangent Segments

When two secants are drawn through a circle from an external point, the lengths of the segments can be found using the rule:

(whole segment) (external part) = (whole segment) (external part)

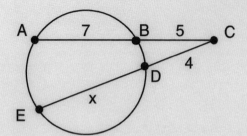

(AC) (BC) = (EC) (DC)
(7 + 5) (5) = (x + 4) (4)
60 = 4x + 16
44 = 4x
11 = x
segment ED = 11; segment EC = 15

The same rule holds true for a secant and a tangent segment:

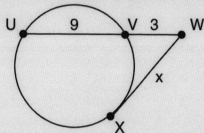

(UW) (VW) = (XW) (XW)
(9 + 3) (3) = (x) (x)
36 = x²
6 = x
segment XW = 6

If two tangents are drawn from the same external point, the tangent segments are congruent:

RS = ST

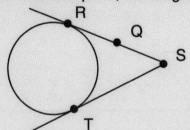

Use the diagrams above and the measures given to find the missing lengths. Then use your answers and the decoder to reveal the name of a teenage inventor and his invention.

A	C	D	E	F	G	H	M	N	O	R	S	T	U	V	W
7	25	17	10	14.4	24	12	9	3	40	4.4	22	30	4	8	20

1. AC = 15, BC = 5, DC = 3; find ED and EC.
2. ED = 20, DC = 4, BC = 8; find EC, AB, and AC.
3. AB = 6, BC = 4, DC = 5; find AC, ED, and EC.
4. UW = 27, VW = 3; find XW.

5. UV = 9, VW = 16; find XW.
6. XW = 12, VW = 10; find UW and UV.
7. VW = 10, XW = 20; find UW and UV.
8. RQ = 10, ST = 17; find RS and QS.

___ ___ ___ ___ ___ ___ ___   ___ ___ ___ ___ ___ ___ ___ ___ ___
1(EC) 2(AC) 3(AC) 1(ED) 7(UV) 3(AC) 6(UV)   2(EC) 6(UV) 3(AC) 3(AC) 3(ED) 5 7(UW) 7(UW) 8(RS)

invented ___ ___ ___ ___ ___ ___ ___ ___ **at the age of**
          3(AC) 8(QS) 6(UV) 4 2(AB) 6(UW) 6(UW) 1(ED)

___ ___ ___ ___ ___ ___ ___ ___ ___ .
1(ED) 3(AC) 3(EC) 3(AC) 3(ED) 7(UV) 3(AC) 3(AC) 3(ED)

Area of a Sector and Arc Length

The area of a sector is a part of the area of the whole circle.
To determine the part (or fraction): divide the central angle of the sector by 360°.
Then: multiply that fraction by πr^2 to find the area of the sector.

Examples:

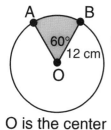

O is the center

the fraction: $\frac{60}{360} = \frac{1}{6}$

the area $= \frac{1}{6} \pi (12)^2$

$= \frac{1}{6} \cdot 144\pi$

$= 24\pi \text{ cm}^2$

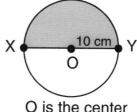

O is the center

the fraction: $\frac{180}{360} = \frac{1}{2}$

the area $= \frac{1}{2} \pi (10)^2$

$= \frac{1}{2} \cdot 100\pi$

$= 50\pi \text{ cm}^2$

Arc length is a part (or fraction) of the circumference. Multiply the fraction by circumference ($2\pi r$) to determine the arc length.

Examples:

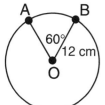

$\overset{\frown}{AB} = \frac{60}{360} \cdot$ circumference

$\overset{\frown}{AB} = \frac{1}{6} \cdot 2\pi (12)$

$= 4\pi \text{ cm}$

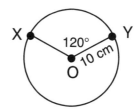

$\overset{\frown}{XY} = \frac{120}{360} \cdot$ circumference

$\overset{\frown}{XY} = \frac{1}{3} \cdot 2\pi (10)$

$= \frac{20}{3} \pi \text{ cm}$

Use the diagram and the radius or diameter given to find the area of the sector or length of the arc named.

1. XQ = 12 cm; find the area of sector XQW.
2. WQ = 9 mm; find the area of sector XQV.
3. XT = 12 cm; find the area of sector UQT.
4. QZ = 10 mm; find the area of sector ZQT.
5. YQ = 16 in.; find the area of sector XQY.
6. XT = 36 mm; find the area of sector VQU.

7. WQ = 18 cm; find the length of $\overset{\frown}{WV}$.
8. QU = 10 in.; find the length of $\overset{\frown}{VU}$.
9. XT = 24 mm; find the length of $\overset{\frown}{YT}$.
10. ZQ = 15 cm; find the length of $\overset{\frown}{YZ}$.
11. XT = 16 cm; find the length of $\overset{\frown}{XZ}$.
12. QW = 30 in.; find the length of $\overset{\frown}{WT}$.

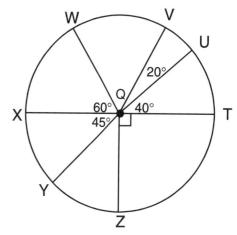

Q is the center
$\overline{XT}$ is a diameter

Surface Area and Volume of Spheres

Surface Area = $4\pi r^2$	Volume = $\frac{4}{3}\pi r^3$
square units	cubic units

Use a straight edge to connect the radius of the sphere to its correct surface area and volume. The letters that remain will reveal the name of the mathematician who made the first scientific attempt to compute the value of π.

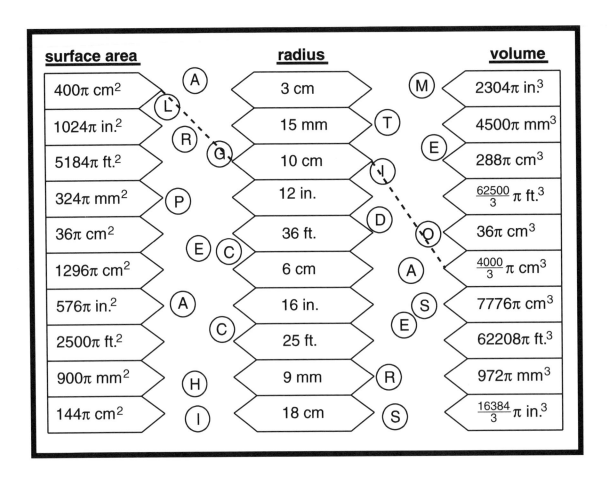

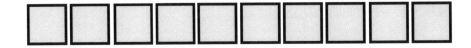

Answer Page

Page 1:

Across
3. straight
5. skew
6. complementary
8. leg
9. perpendicular
10. acute
11. vertical
12. equilateral
15. hypotenuse

Down
1. isosceles
2. right
4. parallel
5. supplementary
6. congruent
7. scalene
13. obtuse
14. four

Page 2:

1. $45°$
2. $62°$
3. $130°$
4. $110°$
5. $70°$
6. $60°$
7. $105°$
8. $75°$
9. $65°$
10. $55°$
11. $52°$
12. $83°$
13. $113°$
14. $140°$
15. $80°$
16. $100°$
17. $68°$

Susan B. Anthony and Benjamin Franklin

Page 3:

Julia Morgan

Page 4:

$A = 117°$
$C = 152°$
$E = 65°$
$F = 25°$
$G = 37°$
$H = 99°$
$I = 81°$
$K = 123°$
$L = 97°$
$N = 40°$
$O = 83°$
$R = 90°$
$S = 120°$
$T = 60°$
$W = 12°$
$Y = 79°$

The coastline of Alaska is longer than the entire coastline of the lower forty–eight states.

Page 5:

1. 5, 19
2. 2, 32
3. 5, 45
4. 1, 7
5. 6, 24
6. 0, 20

Pythagoras

Page 6:

1. $x = 75°$
   $y = 12$
2. $x = 60°$
3. $w = 110°$
   $x = 3$
   $y = 90°$
   $z = 70°$

4. $x = 8$
   $y = 80°$
5. $x = 30°$
   $y = 10$
   $z = 5$
6. $w = 95°$
   $x = 45°$
   $y = 7$
   $z = 85°$

7. $a = 115°$
   $b = 90°$
   $c = 40°$
   $m = 4$
   $x = 25°$
   $y = 65°$

ENIAC

Page 7:

1. $x = 5$
2. $y = 23$
3. $w = 3$
4. $g = -4$
5. $p = 15$
6. $x = 1$
7. $m = -9$
8. $n = 10$
9. $t = 5$
10. $y = \frac{1}{2}$
11. $x = 7$
12. $m = 6$
13. $c = 23$
14. $x = -7$

Answer Page

Page 8:
1. x = 3
2. x = 10
3. x = 5
4. x = 20
5. x = 1
6. x = 13
7. x = 6
8. x = 15
9. x = 65
10. x = 25
11. x = 12
12. x = 17
13. x = 18
14. x = 8
15. x = 30
16. x = 23   **SIX**

Page 9:
1. 15°, 75°
2. 70°, 110°
3. 60°, 120°
4. 32°, 58°
5. 36°, 54°, 144°
6. 45°, 45°
7. 90°, 90°
8. 30°, 60°
9. 50°, 40°
10. 40°, 140°

Page 10:
1. x = 5
2. x = 12
3. x = −6
4. a = 4
5. x = −1
6. x = 7
7. x = 6
8. d = 2
9. k = 10
10. x = 3
11. p = 14
the speed of light

Page 11:
1. (−5, −1)
2. (−4, 0)
3. (−4, −2)
4. (−3, 0)
5. (−2, 2)
6. (0, 2)
7. (2, 2)
8. (4, 2)
The symbol is a radical sign.

Page 12:   Wrigley Field in Chicago   **Page 13:**   Christoff Rudolff

Page 14:
1. 9
2. 3
3. 12
4. 20
5. 10
6. $4\sqrt{2}$
7. 13
8. 26
9. $3\sqrt{3}$
10. $3\sqrt{5}$
11. 25
12. 8
13. 15
14. 17
They are all triangular numbers.

Page 15:   the bicycle   **Page 16:** sixty feet, six inches   **Page 17:** square

Page 18:   Count the number of triangles and multiply by: 180°.
1. 3 Δs, 540°
2. 5 Δs, 900°
3. 2 Δs, 360°
4. 4 Δs, 720°
5. 6 Δs, 1080°
6. 1 Δ, 180°
7. 1440°
8. 1800°
9. 5400°

Page 19:   R. Buckminster Fuller

Page 20:
1. 720°, 120°, 360°, 60°
2. pentagon, 108°, 360°, 72°
3. octagon, 1080°, 360°, 45°
4. 1440°, 144°, 360°, 36°
5. dodecagon, 1800°, 150°, 360°
6. quadrilateral, 360°, 360°, 90°

Page 21:   Gottfried Leibniz   **Page 22:** He invented the zipper.

Page 23:
1. $11\sqrt{3}$
2. $56\sqrt{3} + 14\sqrt{2}$
3. $15\sqrt{2} - 20$
4. $6\sqrt{2}$
5. $5\sqrt{2}$
6. $5\sqrt{3}$
7. 11
8. $8\sqrt{2}$
9. $3\sqrt{10}$
10. $\frac{2}{3}$
11. $\frac{\sqrt{10}}{2}$
12. $\sqrt{2}$
13. $\frac{\sqrt{2}}{2}$
14. $\frac{\sqrt{3}}{3}$

the Babylonians

Answer Page

Page 24:

1. $a = 10$; $b = 5\sqrt{3}$ 4. $a = 3$; $b = 3$ 7. $a = 6\sqrt{3}$; $b = 6\sqrt{3}$

2. $a = 8$; $b = 8\sqrt{2}$ 5. $a = 2\sqrt{2}$; $b = 4$ 8. $a = 12$; $b = 6\sqrt{3}$

3. $a = 6$; $b = 6\sqrt{3}$ 6. $a = 7$ 9. $a = 8\sqrt{2}$; $b = 8\sqrt{2}$

The Harlem Globetrotters

Page 25:

1. 10   4. 50°   7. 12   10. 110°   13. 35°   16. 360°

2. 9   5. 105°   8. 120°   11. 5   14. 60°   **XEROX**

3. 85°   6. 30   9. 23   12. 25   15. 100°

Page 26:

1a. 16   2a. 4   3a. 10   **Page 27:**   3j. 15   5u. 16

  b. 12   b. 120°   b. 90°   1a. 4   k. 17   v. 20

  c. 20   c. 60°   c. $10\sqrt{2}$ b. 5   m. 7   w. 34

  d. 10   d. 60°   d. $5\sqrt{2}$ c. $5\sqrt{3}$ 4n. $3\sqrt{3}$ x. 12

  e. 90°   e. 30°   e. $5\sqrt{2}$ d. 9   p. $3\sqrt{6}$

  f. 30°   f. 30°   f. 90°   2e. $3\sqrt{3}$ q. $3\sqrt{3}$

  g. 10   g. 2   g. 45°   f. 3   r. 10

  h. 30°   h. $2\sqrt{3}$ h. 45°   g. 12   t. 6

  i. 60°   i. 4   i. $10\sqrt{2}$ h. 18   **NEVADA**

Page 28:

1. Always   6. Sometimes   11. Always
2. Never   7. Sometimes   12. Sometimes
3. Always   8. Sometimes   13. Never
4. Always   9. Always   14. Sometimes
5. Sometimes   10. Never   15. Never

Page 29:

1	8		6	0	
2		7	2		8
	4	0			
3	4		1		1
3		5	6		5
2		8		5	0

Page 30:

1. 12 u²   6. 192 u²
2. 40 u²   7. $18\sqrt{3}$ u²
3. 30 u²   8. 81 u²
4. 84 u²   9. 32 u²
5. 52 u²   10. 6 u²

MAINE

Page 31:

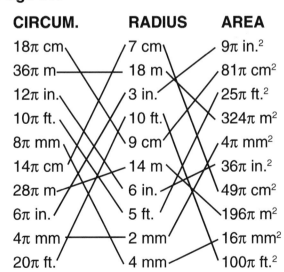

CIRCUM.	RADIUS	AREA
18π cm	7 cm	9π in.²
36π m	18 m	81π cm²
12π in.	3 in.	25π ft.²
10π ft.	10 ft.	324π m²
8π mm	9 cm	4π mm²
14π cm	14 m	36π in.²
28π m	6 in.	49π cm²
6π in.	5 ft.	196π m²
4π mm	2 mm	16π mm²
20π ft.	4 mm	100π ft.²

Ben Franklin

Answer Page

Page 32:
1. 130π ft.²
2. 78π ft.²
3. 440π mm²
4. 100π in.²
5. 294 mm²
6. 486 in.²
7. 236 mm²
8. 592 cm
9. 336 in.²
10. 1120 m²
11. $156 + 60\sqrt{2}$ cm²

Page 33:
1. $375\sqrt{3}$ cm³
2. 1728 mm³
3. 300 cm³
4. 72 cm³
5. 1200 mm³
6. 1200π cm³
7. 5625π mm³
8. 405π cm³
9. 750π mm³
10. 360π cm³
11. 1500π mm³
12. 2640 cm³
13. 240 mm³
14. $360\sqrt{3}$ cm³

John S. Pemberton **invented** Coca Cola.

Page 34/35:
1. 112 cm²
2. 336 mm²
3. $64 + 64\sqrt{3}$ cm²
4. 340 in.²
5. 756 cm²
6. 1360 in.²
7. 220π mm²
8. 375π cm²
9. 189π ft.²
10. 184π in.²
11. 280π mm²
12. 119π ft.²
13. 600π cm²

The states that touch the most other states are Tennessee and Missouri—each touches eight other states.

Page 36: Martha Washington **Page 37:** the cubit **Page 38:** One Out of Many

Page 39: the angles of △ABD add to <u>180°</u>.
1. 50°
2. 70°
3. 110°
4. 180°
5. 60°
6. 60°
7. 50°
8. 70°
9. 55°
10. 100°
11. 65°
12. 60°
13. 60°
14. 150°
15. 80°
16. 185°

Page 40: Wilt Chamberlain

Page 41:
1. XB = 2, AC = 7, DB = 8
2. XC = 4, AC = 14, DB = 13
3. XC = 4, AC = 18, DB = 15
4. XB = 3, AC = 13, DB = 15
5. XC = 8, AC = 14, DB = 16
6. XC = 8, AC = 17, DB = 18
7. DX = 12, XB = 12, AC = 25, DB = 24
8. AX = 10, XC = 10, AC = 20, DB = 25
9. XC = 5, AC = 17, DX = 6
10. XB = 8, DB = 11, XC = 12

Page 42:
1. ED = 22, EC = 25
2. EC = 24, AB = 4, AC = 12
3. AC = 10, ED = 3, EC = 8
4. XW = 9
5. XW = 20
6. UW = 14.4, UV = 4.4
7. UW = 40, UV = 30
8. RS = 17, QS = 7

Chester Greenwood **invented** earmuffs **at the age of** seventeen.

Page 43:
1. 24π cm²
2. 27π mm²
3. 4π cm²
4. 25π mm²
5. 32π in.²
6. 18π mm²
7. 6π cm
8. $\frac{10}{9}\pi$ in.
9. 9π mm
10. $\frac{15}{4}\pi$ cm
11. 4π cm
12. 20π in.

Page 44: **Archimedes**
(see box at right)

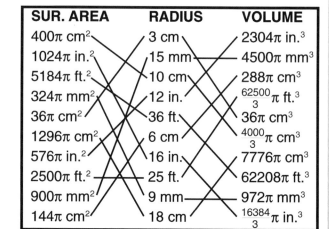

SUR. AREA	RADIUS	VOLUME
400π cm²	3 cm	2304π in.³
1024π in.²	15 mm	4500π mm³
5184π ft.²	10 cm	288π cm³
324π mm²	12 in.	$\frac{62500}{3}\pi$ ft.³
36π cm²	36 ft.	36π cm³
1296π cm²	6 cm	$\frac{4000}{3}\pi$ cm³
576π in.²	16 in.	7776π cm³
2500π ft.²	25 ft.	62208π ft.³
900π mm²	9 mm	972π mm³
144π cm²	18 cm	$\frac{16384}{3}\pi$ in.³